Solving Children's Sleep Problems

A Step by Step Guide for Parents

Lyn Quine

Books on Prescription

First published 1997
by Beckett Karlson Ltd
Westminster House
Ermine Business Park
Huntingdon
Cambs PE18 6XY

A catalogue record of this book is available from the British Library

ISBN 1 901292 01 0

Produced and Distributed by
DSM
The Studio
Denton
Peterborough
Cambs PE7 3SD

Illustrations by Mic Lowen

Author's Acknowledgements

I could not have written this book without the help of a great many people. I am indebted to many research colleagues whose ideas and techniques I made use of while compiling the programmes, to colleagues in the Psychology Department at the University of Kent for their friendship, support and encouragement, to colleagues in the two NHS Trusts who collaborated with the research, and to the charitable foundation that funded the research that the book is based on. In particular I would like to thank Linda Ward and Janet Lewis of the Joseph Rowntree Foundation, Sue Sullivan of South Kent Community Healthcare NHS Trust and Maureen Smith of North Kent Healthcare NHS Trust, and my research colleagues both within the University and outside: Derek Rutter, Ian Albery, Ann Gath, Chris Kiernan, Colin Espie, Greg Stores, David Bramble and John Clements. I should also like to thank the health visitors who helped to test the programmes and all the parents of sleepless children who took part in the research or who have written to me about their experiences. Finally, I should like to thank Jo Oven for her painstaking editorial work on the manuscript.

Publishers' Acknowledgements

The publishers would like to thank those who helped with the illustrative content of the book: Mic Lowen for drawing the cartoons; Hilary Shears for the original ideas for the cartoons on pages 17, 19, 69 and 166; Roy Kelly for the idea for the cartoon on page 12: Marc Lowen for the cover design.

SUPPORTED BY
JR
JOSEPH ROWNTREE FOUNDATION

*The **Joseph Rowntree Foundation** has supported this project as part of its programme of research and innovative development projects, which it hopes will be of value to policy makers and practitioners. The facts presented and views expressed in this book, however are those of the author and not necessarily those of the Foundation.*

CONTENTS

INTRODUCTION 3
How to Use This Book 4
Before You Start 5

PART I SLEEP AND SLEEPLESSNESS 9

Chapter 1 The Sleepless Child 1
What Are Sleep Problems? 11
How Common Are Sleep Problems? 12
Why Are Some Children Prone to Sleep Problems? 13
The Disabled Child 13
Has My Child a Sleep Problem? 14
Why Do I Need to Solve My Child's Sleep Problem? 17

Chapter 2 Sleep and Sleep Processes 21
Normal Sleep 21
The Development of Sleep Stages in Children 22

Chapter 3 Why Sleep Problems Arise 25
Problems Arising from the Way Bedtime Is Handled 25
Disturbances of Sleep Rhythms 33
The Stressed or Anxious Child 34
Medical Conditions 35
Events that Disrupt Sleep — The Parasomnias 38
Sleep Problems — An Overview 39

Chapter 4 Taking a Sleep History 41
An Example 44

PART II HOW TO CHANGE YOUR CHILD'S NIGHT-TIME BEHAVIOUR 47

Chapter 1 Analysing Your Child's Behaviour 49
Understanding Difficult Night-time Behaviour: The ABC Analysis 50
B is for Behaviour 50
C is for Consequences 53
A is for Antecedents 57
Consolidating Learning 59
Chapter 2 Four Strategies for Changing Behaviour 61
1. Positive Reinforcement 61
2. Providing the Conditions that Encourage Sleep 65
3. Extinction 68
4. Gradual Stages of Change (Graduated Extinction) 71
Points to Remember 73
Test Your Knowledge of Behavioural Methods 74

PART III IDENTIFYING YOUR CHILD'S SLEEP PROBLEM 79

How To Use The Charts 81
Chartfinder 82
Diagnostic Charts 83

PART IV SOLVING YOUR CHILD'S SLEEP PROBLEM 113

Advice on How To Carry Out a Programme 115
Talking to Your Child 115
Some Questions 116
Advice on How to Settle Your Baby to Sleep 117

Limit Setting Problems 119
Programme 1 121
Programme 2 123
Programme 3 124
Programme 4 126
Programme 5 127
Programme 6 128
Incorrect Sleep Associations 130
Programme 7 133
Programme 8 135
Programme 9 137
Programme 10 138
Anxieties or Night Time Fears 140
Programme 11 142
Programme 12 143
Difficulty Adjusting To Stress 149
Programme 13 151
Programme 14 152
Night Time Feeding Problems 155
Programme 15 157
Food Allergies 160
Programme 16 161
Irregular Sleep-Wake Patterns 162
Programme 17 163
Late Sleep Phase 166
Programme 18 168
Programme 19 171
Programme 20 173
Early Sleep Phase 174
Programme 21 175
Insufficient Sleep 177
Programme 22 178
Poor Sleep Hygiene 179
Programme 23 181
Environmental Sleep Disturbance 183
Programme 24 184
Obstructive Sleep Apnoea 185
Confusional Arousals 187
Sleepwalking (Somnambulism) 190
Sleep Terrors 192
Programme 25 193
Sleep Starts 196
Sleep Talking 197
Nightmares and Anxiety Dreams 198
Programme 26 199
Headbanging or Bodyrocking 201
Programme 27 202
Sleep Bruxism (Tooth Grinding) 204
Sleep Enuresis (Bedwetting) 205
Programme 28 209
Programme 29 209
Apnoea of Prematurity and Infancy 211
Colic 213
Two Other Common Problems That Cause Sleep Disturbance 215

INDEX 216

INTRODUCTION

Introduction

Right from the day Joe was born he would not go to sleep unless he was in someone's arms. The trouble starts when you try to put him in bed on his own. He will scream and cry. Sometimes he stays in his own bed at bedtime, but a couple of hours later he wakes up crying and comes straight to our room. He gets into bed with us and cuddles up so close that I can't move for the rest of the night. If you try to move him over he wakes up whingeing and crying. Once he wakes up he seems to know that the more noise he makes the quicker we will do what he wants so as not to wake our other two children. Quite frequently I have had all three in bed with me. My husband seems to spend every night on the sofa and our marriage is suffering because we both sleep badly and seem to spend a lot of time bickering, which doesn't help matters. Please can you help?

Peter is two-and-a-half years old. He starts the night off in his own bed, but only stays there for a little while. He comes downstairs and usually falls asleep on the settee. Every night he comes to bed with us. We have tried to stop this but he gets really restless and angry. Anything you can do to help would be appreciated.

Mary is two. She sleeps very badly, waking up every two or three hours and crying very loudly. She goes to sleep on her side with one of us rubbing her back. She has to be asleep before we can leave the room. This happens every night and I can't cope any more. Please help us. We feel very alone with our problem.

These descriptions of sleep problems are examples from letters received from parents over the last few years which made me decide to write this book. Many children have sleep patterns that are a problem for their parents. Sleep problems seriously disrupt family life, and lead to tiredness, irritability, limitations of the parents' activities, and frequently marital discord. Stress and depression, which are common in parents with very young children, can be made worse by a lack of sleep. Tired parents are unable to think up rational ways of coping with their child's night-time wakings and often resort to shouting, smacking, and punishment.

Only 25 years ago little was known about sleep problems and few treatments were available. Recently great advances have been made in what is known about children's sleep and what can go wrong with it. The trouble is that not enough of this information has reached parents. There are many things that parents could do to improve their child's sleep if only they had the information. That is why I have written this book.

The ideas in it are based on several years of extensive research into the treatment of sleep problems funded by the Rowntree Foundation and on experience of helping many parents who read about the research and got in touch with us. Our research has shown that these methods really work. We tested them in a controlled trial of families of children with the most difficult and persistent sleep problems we could find — a group of children with physical and mental handicaps. There were dramatic results. Improvement was shown in every single child, and 80% of the children's sleep problems either resolved completely or improved very markedly. The sleep problems of a control group of children who did not receive treatment did not improve.

After the trial had ended our research team began to be approached by many parents of children without handicaps, and we found that the methods worked just as well for them. Many families have now used the programmes to improve their children's sleep problems. I hope that this book will help more parents to do the same.

How to Use This Book

The book provides a complete teaching programme that you can use to help your child to develop and maintain better sleep patterns. It will help you

- to understand why problems occur and how to avoid them.
- to diagnose your child's sleep problem.
- to carry out easy step-by-step programmes that will resolve your child's problem.

The book is organised in four sections. Part I, 'Sleep and Sleeplessness', gives some general information about sleep problems — what they are, how commonly they occur, and how to recognise if your child has one. The causes of sleep problems are examined, and suggestions are offered for basic sleep hygiene — ways of encouraging children to develop more desirable bedtime behaviour from an early age.

In Part II, 'How to Change Your Child's Night-time Behaviour', the principles behind the approach are explained so that you can understand why the programmes work so effectively. You will be taught how to analyse your child's bedtime behaviour and how to use the techniques described to resolve his sleep problem. The book is illustrated with many examples of children who have used the programmes, although the names have been changed so that individual families cannot be identified.

Part III, 'Identifying Your Child's Sleep Problem', contains a set of symptom charts which provide a unique and easy way of pinpointing the exact problem your child is suffering from. Once you have found the chart dealing with the symptom that is troubling you, a series of simple 'Yes' or 'No' questions will lead you to a diagnosis. The chart will then refer you to a section of Part IV, 'Solving Your Child's Sleep Problem', giving a full description of the problem and information on how to solve it including, where appropriate, step-by-step programmes specially developed for that problem.

Sleep problems are rather like medical conditions: they have a name, a history, specific symptoms, predisposing factors, and successful treatments. To categorise sleep problems we use the framework provided in the International Classification of Sleep Disorders (1990), which is the most recent classification available.

Before You Start

How Good Is Your Child's General Health?

Begin by asking your doctor to check your child's general health. It is important first to find out whether there might be some medical condition associated with the sleep problem, and if so to get it treated. Some medical conditions quite commonly found in children, such as colic, cow's milk allergy, or ear infections, produce symptoms such as pain or diarrhoea which can result in sleeplessness. Although distressing, these are not true sleep problems. Any chronic condition such as asthma, diabetes, cystic fibrosis, or epilepsy may contribute to persistent sleep problems. The problems may be directly caused by the illness, or may be an indirect result of medication, discomfort, or anxieties. While none of these conditions means that your child's sleep problems cannot be improved, it is important that any treatable problem receives appropriate care. For this reason it is advisable to check with your doctor before starting a sleep programme. Very often, however, children who have had illnesses such as teething problems or colic, who have suffered stressful events, or who are just slower to develop a regular sleep cycle, develop unusual habits around sleep. The habits that form when your child is ill may persist even when the original problem has got better. The child has come to expect and enjoy the extra attention he has received. When this happens you will have to help your child relearn the 'rules' of good night-time behaviour. Very occasionally sleep problems can be the first sign of a medical disorder such as a kidney problem, so it is important to make sure that your child is healthy before starting a programme.

Taking a Sleep Diary

Before you begin a programme to solve your child's sleep problem it is important to collect what is known as 'baseline information' on the problem by filling in a sleep diary. This is necessary for two reasons: firstly, it will give you the precise information on your child's sleep patterns that you will need to diagnose the problem correctly, and secondly, when you begin a programme it will help you to get an accurate picture of the progress you have made and so encourage you to keep going. There is a sleep diary on the next page that you can photocopy. It has spaces for you to fill in details such as the time that your child goes to sleep each night, what you do to settle him to sleep, the time taken to settle, and the length and number of night-time wakings. As you read on in this book and learn more about sleep problems it is likely that you will begin to change the way you respond to your child's difficult night-time behaviour — you will start to treat the problem. In order to get a true picture of the problem as it is before treatment, **please begin filling in the sleep diary NOW.**

SLEEP DIARY

NAME... WEEK.........................

Day and Date	Day 1	Day 2	Day 3	Day 4	Day 5	Day 6	Day 7
Time woke in morning							
Time and length of nap(s) in day							
Time started preparing for bed Any problems here? What did you do?							
Time went to bed at night and where How long did child take to settle? What did you do?							
Time went to sleep							
How many times did the child wake? (Note length of each waking) For how long was the child awake altogether? What did you do?							

PART I

SLEEP AND SLEEPLESSNESS

Chapter 1

The Sleepless Child

What Are Sleep Problems?

The most common sleep problems are settling and waking problems. **Settling** problems are difficulties in getting the child to bed and settled to sleep. Some children will not go to bed and settle to sleep alone, and instead fall asleep downstairs or go to bed at the same time as their parents. Some will only go to sleep if the parent lies down with them or if they are being rocked. Others keep coming downstairs or insist on a prolonged bedtime ritual. Settling problems can be very exhausting for parents who are unable to have any time to themselves at the end of the day. **Waking problems** are when sleep is disrupted after the child has gone to bed. Sometimes children wake up frequently during the night and disturb their parents by calling for attention. Sometimes they wake only once or twice, but cannot be resettled easily. Some children keep coming into their parents' bedroom and creeping into their bed. Sometimes they wake up very early in the morning and wake their parents. Severe lack of sleep can cause enormous stress to parents, especially those who are already tired out by the extra work of caring for a child with mental or physical disability.

Settling and waking problems can be caused by a variety of factors, and their treatment varies accordingly. The child may never have learned to go to sleep on his own, or he may be afraid to go to sleep alone because he has been alarmed by a frightening film or story. He may have been distressed by events that have happened in the family: illness, divorce, moving house, or a new baby. There may be a medical cause for his sleeplessness — a food allergy or an ear infection. If the sleep problem has become persistent, he may just have got used to the cuddles and attention he had when he was ill or upset and want them to continue. He will need supportive firmness to encourage him to settle to sleep and sleep through the night without disturbing his parents.

In addition to settling and waking problems, children sometimes show other symptoms of sleep disturbance. These include excessive sleepiness during the day, feeling tired unusually early or not going to sleep until unusually late, night-time fears, strange movements during sleep, sleep talking, sleep walking, sleep terrors, nightmares and bedwetting. Many of these problems are rare, and children often grow out of them. Some require treatment because they affect the child's daytime functioning and disturb the parents' sleep. Children wake at other times when they are sick, teething, frightened, or in pain, or when there have been disruptions in their home life, and these are not true sleep problems. At these times children need comfort, not discipline, and they will soon settle back to sleeping soundly again.

How Common Are Sleep Problems?

Sleep problems are very common in children under the age of 12 years. Studies have estimated that up to 20% of 2 year old children and 5% of 8 year old children wake regularly during the night. Settling problems occur in approximately 20% of 1-2 year olds and 12% of 8 year olds. About 6% of 3 year olds and 5% of 8 year olds also sleep regularly in their parents' bed.

Children with physical and mental handicaps seem to be particularly likely to present sleep problems. In a study of learning disabled children aged 0-18 we found that 67% had waking problems, more than half of them waking every night, and 51% had settling problems, about two-thirds taking two hours or more to settle to sleep at night. During this time a variety of behaviours were displayed from shouting and screaming, crying, and tantrums, to repeatedly getting up again, coming downstairs, throwing toys around the bedroom, scattering toys and possessions out of drawers, or destructive behaviour such as ripping off wallpaper or smearing the bathroom with shampoo or toothpaste. The sleep problems were very persistent: 48% of the settling problems and 64% of the waking problems had not resolved three years later.

Why Are Some Children Prone to Sleep Problems?

Children differ widely in their ability to go to sleep or stay asleep. Some children sleep well from birth, but others seem more prone to sleep problems and any changes in bedtime routine, illness or holidays may disrupt their sleep patterns. Some doctors argue that treatment is unnecessary since the problems have their roots in the child's stage of development and will eventually be outgrown. Our own research has shown, however, that whilst many problems do get better with time, a substantial number are very persistent, particularly if the child has a mental or physical handicap or a chronic illness.

As to why particular children seem to be vulnerable, it has been suggested that problems at birth and length of labour, which lead to irritability, temperamental factors, anxiety or depression in parents, or stress in the home may predispose a child to sleep problems. Our own research has shown that parents of children with sleep problems are more likely than other mothers to respond in certain ways when their child wakes at night. They are more likely to attend to the child immediately by offering drinks, cuddles, and attention, and are less likely to allow the child to cry for a few minutes, to play music to help the child to settle, or to read him a bedtime story. It seems that the readier the mother is to offer comfort at night, the worse the sleep pattern of the child. Our research has shown that sleep improves dramatically when parents are taught new management techniques.

The Disabled Child

There are a number of reasons why disabled children tend to be prone to sleep disturbance. Children with learning disabilities take longer than other children to learn the 'rules' of appropriate bedtime behaviour. They often have limited use and understanding of communication and are therefore more difficult to teach. Damage to the central nervous system can sometimes cause quite profound disturbances of the sleep-wake cycle that are persistent and difficult to treat. Physical impairments, too, increase the likelihood that a child will have a sleep problem. Disabled children may have difficulty getting comfortable at night and find it hard to change position; they may experience discomfort at night due to muscle spasm; they may be incontinent or have breathing difficulties or skin irritations that disturb them at night. Children with sensory impairments may not receive the same cues that bedtime is approaching: blind children do not see darkness fall, for example. Epilepsy may disrupt a child's sleeping patterns, as may medication for the condition. A frequent difficulty for parents of children with disability or illness is that they are often more anxious about their child. This sometimes leads them to change their normal patterns of child-rearing, which may unintentionally encourage sleep problems. The parent of a child who has epilepsy or has been seriously ill may go to him at night if there is the slightest noise, or even simply to check that he is alright, and this will make the child slow to learn that night-time is for sleeping.

If you are the parent of a disabled child you may think that disturbed sleep patterns are an integral part of the child's handicap — a problem you are stuck with and have to tolerate as best you can. In fact, damage to the mechanisms that control sleep patterns occurs in relatively few children. More often, their sleep scheduling has become disordered, or they have simply failed to learn the rules of appropriate night-time behaviour. Most children can be helped to develop and maintain more regular sleep patterns by following the programmes in this book.

Has My Child a Sleep Problem?

Deciding on whether your child has a sleep problem is an individual matter. What seems to one family to be a desperate sleep problem may not concern the next. A sleep problem is only really a problem if the well-being, health, or happiness of any family member is compromised. If your child's sleep patterns cause significant problems for you, your child, or the rest of the family, then he has a sleep problem.

Here are some early warning signs to help you to recognise the presence of sleep problems.

In the Child (children over six months)

- When your child refuses to go to bed, engages in bedtime battles, or takes a long time to settle to sleep more than two or three times a week.
- When your child refuses to go to sleep unless you lie down with him more than two or three times a week.
- When your child comes downstairs repeatedly or calls out for you more than two or three times a week.
- When you find your child's bedtimes getting progressively later.
- When your child wakes repeatedly in the night crying or calling out for you more than two or three times a week.
- When your child is awake regularly for long periods at night.

- ❖ When your child repeatedly comes into your bedroom or insists on sharing your bed on a regular basis.
- ❖ When your child wakes very early in the morning more than two or three times a week.

In Yourself

- ❖ When you find yourself giving in for the sake of peace and quiet more than just occasionally.
- ❖ When the thought of putting your child to bed makes you feel apprehensive.
- ❖ When you start having frequent negative feelings towards your child at night-time.
- ❖ When you start to feel tired all the time.

- ❖ When you first find yourself shouting too loudly at your child at bedtime or during the night.
- ❖ When you and your partner start to argue about your child's bedtime behaviour.
- ❖ When you begin to be tempted to smack your child to make him stay in bed.

If you are experiencing several of these things in your family and feel you may be losing control of the situation, your child's behaviour, and your own emotions, then your child probably has a sleep problem.

Some children do not get enough sleep, and often the first question that parents ask is 'How much sleep does my child really need?'. The amount of sleep children need varies tremendously. Some children are short sleepers while some are long sleepers. The table below shows the average amount of sleep taken during the day and night by children in one of our studies. This will give you a rough estimate of how much sleep your child needs. But if your child sleeps well and appears to be alert and active in the morning you have no need to worry if he sleeps less than this. If he appears tired and bad tempered in the morning, however, and sleepy during the day, then he is not getting enough sleep.

Average Sleep Needs

Age	Average Number of Hours Sleep Needed		Age	Average Number of Hours Sleep Needed	
	Daytime	Night-time		Daytime	Night-time
1 week	8	8½	7 years	—	10½
4 weeks	6¾	8¾	8 years	—	10¼
3 months	5	10	9 years	—	10
6 months	4	10	10 years	—	9¾
9 months	2¾	11¼	11 years	—	9½
12 months	2½	11½	12 years	—	9¼
2 years	1¼	11¾	13 years	—	9¼
3 years	1	11	14 years	—	9
4 years	—	11½	15 years	—	8¾
5 years	—	11	16 years	—	8½
6 years	—	10¾			

It is also sometimes difficult for parents to know when the child should be sleeping through the night, and not waking to be fed. By about 3 or 4 months most healthy babies are sleeping through the night, and by 6 months all babies should be able to do so. If your baby does not sleep through the night by 6 months on most nights, or if he starts waking after sleeping well for a few months, he has a sleep problem.

Why Do I Need to Solve My Child's Sleep Problem?

Sleep problems cause great stress in the family. Parents of children who do not sleep well soon feel frustrated, anxious, and angry. After a few weeks with poor sleep your tiredness and fatigue will affect your daytime behaviour and you will be increasingly tense and edgy with your family. You may find it difficult to pay attention to what you are doing, particularly if it is repetitive, and your reaction time will be slowed down. If your child has a persistent problem you will start to feel tired all the time, irritable, tense, and sometimes tearful. You might start to have microsleeps — little lapses of attention when your brain goes to sleep for 5-10 seconds and then wakes up again.

Sleep deprivation produces all kinds of symptoms of stress. The most common are worry, tiredness, backache, and being easily upset. Some parents get worried that they will punish their child too harshly because they have become so on edge. When a child sleeps badly it is easy for tired parents to get cross with each other, each blaming the other for the child's problem, until their marriage starts to suffer. Parents of a child with sleep problems have little time for themselves or each other. If the child stays awake late into the evening or wakes during the night, many of the relaxing activities that the parents enjoy together are made impossible.

Following treatment for sleep problems, a number of other improvements occur. We have shown in our research that when the child's sleep problems are resolved mothers are less stressed and show increased satisfaction with their marriages, report less irritability, and smack their children less frequently. They feel more positive, more confident, more in control, and more relaxed. The children too are happier, more affectionate, and more able to manage on their own. They have fewer temper tantrums and better concentration, and are easier to handle.

For school aged children sleep problems may interfere with many aspects of their life. Children who are tired during the day may have difficulty concentrating in school and may have behavioural problems in the classroom. At home they may be difficult to manage, throw temper tantrums, or quarrel with brothers and sisters. Children with physical impairments, learning disabilities, or chronic illness already have enough to cope with without the addition of unnecessary sleep problems.

If you have a child in your family with sleep problems, this guide will almost certainly help you to improve your child's sleep patterns and to get a better night's sleep yourself. You may have already received a good deal of advice from other people: relatives, friends, even a doctor or health visitor. You may have been advised to let the child 'cry it out', to make sure that he is particularly tired before you put him to bed, to allow him to share your bed, or to get your doctor to prescribe sleep medication. You may have tried a variety of these strategies but still find that the problem persists. You feel tired, exhausted and hopeless. Not only are you chronically deprived of sleep at night-time, but you have to cope with a tired, irritable, and unreasonable child during the daytime. It doesn't have to be like this. Using the methods described in this book most parents have been able to improve their children's settling and waking patterns. Even if your child suffers from mental or physical disability or chronic illness you can help him to develop more regular sleep habits. The information you will find in this book will help you to identify your child's particular problem and show you how to solve it. The most important thing to bear in mind is that it is *not your fault* that your child has a sleep problem. There are all sorts of reasons why children develop problems, particularly those children with disabilities and chronic illesses, which we discuss on pages 35-38. It is important, however, that parents are sure that they want a cure for the problem and are prepared to work at it. Sometimes parents ask for advice about their child's sleep problem, but they are only interested if it involves no effort on their part. Although they seem to be motivated, they find innumerable reasons why anything that is suggested won't work, or can't be tried out. Unfortunately there is no magic cure. The programmes all involve a certain amount of patience, time, and persistence on your part, but the rewards will be well worth the effort.

There is no magic cure!

CHAPTER 2

SLEEP AND SLEEP PROCESSES

Normal Sleep

Before we can consider how sleep problems in children arise, it is important to understand normal sleep patterns and their development in young children.

Surprisingly, it is still not well understood why people need sleep and what function sleep serves. We know that sleep refreshes our bodies and our minds, that without it we feel tired, and that it is necessary for normal functioning during the day. We also know that there are sleep centres in the brain which control its activity. These determine the twenty-four hour cycles of sleep and wakefulness called the **circadian rhythm**. While the body sleeps the brain continues to work, stimulated by an increased blood flow to it. One of its functions, particularly in childhood and adolescence, is to secrete from the pituitary gland growth hormone which is essential for physical development. Researchers believe that many other important tasks are being performed during sleep which are not yet understood.

Sleep is divided into two distinct states: **REM, or rapid-eye-movement sleep**, and **non-REM sleep**. During the night several cycles of sleep occur.

Non-REM Sleep

Non-REM sleep has four stages which represent progressive levels of sleep from drowsiness to very deep sleep. These can be identified by monitoring brain waves, eye movement and muscle tone.

As a person begins to fall asleep, **Stage I** is entered. This is a state of drowsiness lasting a few minutes in which thoughts begin to drift and awareness of the external world begins to fade, and slow rolling movements begin behind their eyelids. There is an even rhythm of electrical activity in the brain. As a person moves from drowsiness to deeper sleep, a sudden jerk may briefly jolt them into wakefulness. This is called a sleep start and is quite normal.

Arrival at **Stage II** can only be identified by monitoring the brain waves. Large slow waves start to appear interspersed with short bursts of rapid activity. This stage is light sleep and accounts for about half the total of sleep. It is easy to wake someone in this stage, and they might even be unaware of having fallen asleep.

As a person falls more deeply asleep, **Stage III** is entered. It takes a much louder noise to waken a sleeper by this stage. People who are woken deliberately cannot remember anything.

Finally **Stage IV** appears. In this stage the brain waves are longer and slower, heart rate and blood pressure drop, as does body temperature, and breathing slows.

Stages III and IV sleep are the main kinds of sleep that allow the body to recover. If the sleeper is woken during these stages, he or she will be confused and unable to think clearly for some minutes. In non-REM sleep the sleeper's muscles are relaxed and he or she lies still because the brain is not sending messages to the muscles telling them to move. Sleepwalking, night terrors and headbanging during sleep are exceptions to this rule and occur during partial waking.

REM Sleep

REM sleep is entered after one or two cycles in non-REM sleep. In this state breathing and heart rate become irregular, the body uses more oxygen, there is more blood flow to the brain, and the brain waves become quite active. The mind is now 'awake' but in a dream state. Nerve impulses that normally pass down the spinal cord to the muscles become blocked and the body is effectively paralysed. The only muscles unaffected are those controlling eye movement, breathing, and hearing. Some of the stronger signals still reach the muscles, however, and these result in twitching of the hands or legs.

An important feature of REM sleep is bursts of rapid eye movement during which heart rate, blood pressure, breathing rate, and blood flow to the brain increase. If the sleeper is woken during this stage he or she may be able to remember having a dream. Studies of people deliberately deprived of REM sleep have suggested that its functions include information processing and storage, and it is therefore concerned with mental recovery. REM sleep occurs about every 90 minutes in adults and about every 60 minutes in young children. The first REM period of the night is short — about 5 minutes — the second lasts about 10 minutes, and the third about 15 minutes. The final dream period of the night usually lasts between 30 minutes and an hour. Everybody dreams several times each night, although they may not be able to remember the dreams unless they wake from them.

The Development of Sleep Stages in Children

Sleep Patterns in Babies

Sleep patterns begin to develop in babies even before birth. REM sleep can be seen at about 6 or 7 months' gestation, and non-REM between

7 and 8 months. Sleep occupies a major part of the life of young children. A newborn baby spends about 70% of every 24 hours in sleep. By contrast, adults spend only 25-30% of their time sleeping. Sleep in babies varies significantly from sleep in adults, and probably serves a different purpose.

In babies, as in adults, two distinct states can be identified: REM and non-REM sleep. During REM sleep sucking movements are common and fine twitches are continuous with smiles and tremors also occurring. Movements can be seen beneath the eyelids. Occasionally the baby stretches her body or limbs. In non-REM sleep, on the other hand, there is minimal movement, and the baby breathes deeply and lies still.

Non-REM sleep in babies is somewhat different from the non-REM sleep of older children. The brain waves are seen as large slow waves occurring in bursts rather that in a continuous flow. Also it has not yet divided in four stages. By 2 months of age a sequence of sleep stages can be identified, and by 4 months of age a 24-hour sleep-wake rhythm has developed.

Babies spend much more time in REM sleep than adults. In premature babies it accounts for four-fifths of total sleep time and in full term babies a half. By age 3, only a third of sleep is REM sleep, and the adult level of a quarter is reached in early adolescence. During REM or active sleep a child is easily woken, but as her quiet or non-REM sleep increases she is able to sleep for longer periods without waking. The average newborn baby sleeps in a series of short periods for about 16 hours a day. By 16 weeks the child's sleep requirement is down to 14 or 15 hours in three or four longer sleeping periods. By about 4-6 months of age a regular sleep-wake rhythm has developed and the child will sleep through the night — around 12 hours in total. She will still have naps during the day, however. Sleeping through the night does not mean that the child never wakes up, but if she does, she should be able to go back to sleep without disturbing her parents. The pattern of settling varies considerably with each child. Some babies learn to settle quite quickly, but others are much more difficult and are described as 'poor sleepers' from an early stage.

Sleep Cycles in Children

Once the child takes most of her sleep in one block during the night the patterns of sleep stage cycling we have described earlier emerge. By about three months of age, the child will enter non-REM sleep first, rapidly moving through the lighter stages of sleep into Stage IV usually within about ten minutes. In a child this is extremely deep sleep from which it is very difficult to wake her. The Stage IV sleep will continue for about an hour, after which there will be a short arousal. The child will move, turn over or perhaps mutter a little. She may open her eyes or sit up before returning to sleep. There are a number of behaviours that may sometimes occur during these arousals. Some are quite normal, like those described above, but others include sleepwalking, sleep terrors and perhaps bedwetting. The partial waking may only last for a few seconds or minutes. After this there may be a few minutes' drowsiness and then a short period of REM sleep, followed by another cycle of non-REM sleep. Around an hour later there will be another arousal followed by a longer period of REM sleep. During the REM sleep there may be several brief arousals where the child moves, perhaps turns over or pulls the blankets round her, and goes back to sleep. These wakings occur in all children and adults. They are quite normal but sometimes the child is unable to get back to sleep because the conditions she associates with falling asleep are not present. This is when waking problems occur.

After the REM period, another period of non-REM sleep follows and then another slower drifting into Stages III and IV followed by another arousal and another period of REM sleep. Then the rest of the night is spent alternating between REM sleep and Stage II sleep. Young children often move into Stage III or IV just before they wake in the morning.

CHAPTER 3

WHY SLEEP PROBLEMS ARISE

The causes of sleeplessness in children are different from the causes of sleeplessness in adults, and different approaches are needed for identifying and solving them. Sleeplessness in children may stem from problems with the way bedtime is handled, from psychological stress, from medical conditions, from disturbances of the mechanisms that control the timing of sleep in the 24-hour day, or from a combination of these. The following chapter will help you to understand why sleep problems arise and enable you to identify the likely cause of your own child's sleep problems. The descriptions of the sleep problems have been kept as brief as possible here as they will not all be relevant to your child. Full details on specific problems can be found in Part IV.

Problems Arising from the Way Bedtime Is Handled

The Importance of Bedtime Routines

Many settling problems arise because a child has not developed regular sleep habits. Differences exist between cultures, ethnic groups and families in the sleep habits that children are taught. In some societies the child is tightly swaddled when she is put to sleep, while in others she sleeps naked. She may sleep in her own room alone or she may be put to sleep on her mother's shoulder. Other members of the family may share her room or bed. There is no right or wrong way to manage bedtime. If you have a bedtime routine that is working for you and your child is falling asleep easily, sleeping through the night and getting enough sleep, there is no reason to change it. However, there are some routines that will help your child to develop regular habits and to avoid problems in the future. Even if you and your partner are happy to share your bed at night with your child while she is small, as she grows older the habit will probably disturb your sleep and the child's and you will not want it to continue. Similarly, although you may be prepared to get up several times in the night to comfort your child when she is a baby, your patience is eventually likely to wear thin if she continues to wake in the night. Routines at bedtime can help the child to develop sensible settling and waking patterns. If your child is rocked to sleep he may have difficulty going back to sleep alone when he wakes in the night. Instead of quietly going back to sleep he may fuss, cry, and call out for attention. To help him with these night-time wakings, you may have to change his bedtime routine, so that he learns to settle to sleep alone, in his own bed, and can resettle himself after night-time wakings. Routines are important as your child gets older too. They provide a cue to your child that bedtime is approaching and help him to anticipate it.

Lee was two and a half. His mother had had such difficulties settling him at bedime that she started getting him ready for bed straight after tea. He would play about in his pyjamas for about two hours. When bedtime came he always resisted strongly, screaming and kicking wildly as he was carried to bed. Lee had not learned to anticipate bedtime. Setting up a bedtime routine helped him to understand that bedtime was approaching.

If the bedtime routine is a pleasant one, your child will look forward to bedtime instead of becoming more fractious and difficult as it approaches. A bedtime routine should allow you to spend some quiet time with your child. She should know when her bedtime is and when she has to prepare for bed. Bedtime can be made enjoyable and relaxing and your child should know that she has your undivided attention for half an hour or more. When she is ready for bed you can carry out some special activities with your child: have a cuddle, a quiet talk, play some relaxing music, read a bedtime story, or look at a book together. You should avoid noisy games, rough play, and frightening fairy tales. Your child should learn that the routine will not be prolonged. You have set some limits for the routine and will follow them. Don't give in to pleas for 'just one more' story or cuddle. If both you and your child know what to expect there should not be the bedtime struggles and arguments that arise when there is uncertainty. The conditions and practices that promote effective sleep are known as **sleep hygiene**. The guidelines shown below will help your child to develop and maintain good sleep hygiene.

Developing Good Sleep Hygiene

1. *Make sure that the child's room is quiet and dark.*
2. *Wake the child at a regular hour each morning, so that circadian cycling is strengthened.*
3. *Keep a regular bedtime for the child.*
4. *Keep room temperature to a comfortable level. High temperatures disturb sleep.*
5. *Environmental noise should be kept to a minimum (no loud TVs).*
6. *Make sure that the child does not go to bed hungry, but do not give a child over 6 months old feeds/drinks during the night.*
7. *Help the child to learn to fall asleep alone in his/her own bed, without your presence.*
8. *Avoid stimulating activity in the hour before bedtime.*
9. *Do not let the child have prolonged naps in the late afternoon. If the child still needs to sleep, schedule the nap for early afternoon.*
10. *Avoid drinks of cola, chocolate, tea and coffee before bedtime.*

Sleeping in the Parents' Bed

Sleeping in the parents' bed is frequently a source of problems. Some parents are happy to share their bed with their offspring. If you sleep deeply or are lucky enough to have children who do not wriggle or kick, you may enjoy having your children in bed with you at night. If this is the case, it is your decision. Most parents, however, wish to share their bed together alone. Mothers, and particularly fathers, resent small children making a regular appearance in their bedroom late at night or in the small hours of the morning. Most children are incapable of lying still and once they have wheedled their way into their parents' bed they keep both parents awake by wriggling about. Parents get short of sleep and temper, sometimes each blaming the other for failing to discipline the child. Sometimes the mother is blamed because she has allowed the child to share her bed for company while her husband is away.

Most children are incapable of lying still!

It is pleasant for children to have an early morning cuddle in their parents' bed when it is time to get up, but parents who allow a child to share their bed at night may be storing up trouble for themselves later. Peace and privacy at night are important for parents, particularly when their children are young and take up a great deal of time and attention during the day. As the child gets older, it becomes more uncomfortable to have him share your bed and more difficult to evict him. Where sleep is concerned it is best to get into a good routine from the start.

Adam kept coming into his parents' bed during the night. He would lie between his parents and wriggle all night, preventing them from getting a proper night's sleep. His parents were at the end of their tether. Adam's problem was solved by carrying out Programme 4 on page 126.

Sometimes parents choose to share their bed with their child—perhaps they are single parents, or have a partner who travels regularly or who works shifts. They find the presence of the child comforting because it makes them feel less lonely or afraid at night. Sometimes having the child in bed helps parents avoid marital tension or sexual intimacy. If you are one of these parents, you should examine your own feelings carefully. You may be using your child to avoid confronting your own problems, and you are not helping him learn to separate himself from you and see himself as an independent person. It is easy for the whole family to begin to suffer if this pattern continues. You will need to learn to resolve your own needs and problems, perhaps with the help of a Relate counsellor.

Setting Limits for Bedtime Behaviour

Young children frequently display settling problems because parents have found it difficult to be firm with their child and to set limits for the child's bedtime behaviour. About 5-10% of children are thought to experience these problems. Parents complain of difficulty settling the child at night or struggles at bedtime. Sometimes the child will not go to bed and is allowed to fall asleep downstairs in a chair or on the sofa. A famous study of childcare in Nottingham found that many parents reported 'indulging' their children at bedtime and tackling problems in inconsistent ways with short term ends in view. Five per cent of 1 year olds went to bed after 9.30 pm, some at the same time as their parents. Some children regularly started their night's sleep on the sofa, and 43% were left with a dummy or bottle in bed. Fifty-nine per cent were brought downstairs again if they did not settle to sleep, and 33% were taken into the parents' bed for comfort if they woke in the night.

Five year old Joe always put up a struggle at bedtime. When his mother told him it was time to go to bed he would cry and scream until she gave in and let him stay up. His bedtime got later and later, until he went to bed at the same time as his parents. His mother and father did not have any time to themselves at the end of the day. Joe's problem was solved by setting up a regular bedtime routine. His parents set an appropriate bedtime and made it clear to him that he could not stay up. His mother read him a story and gave him some special time to himself. For a few evenings Joe cried and kept coming downstairs, but his parents took him straight back to bed each time and he soon gave up and stayed in bed.

Sometimes a child will not stay in bed, coming downstairs repeatedly or calling out for his parents. Although he may be physiologically ready for sleep, his parents easily give in to his fussing and whining and find it difficult to insist on bedtime routines and regular bedtimes. As a result, he does not go to bed until very late, or does not stay in bed for long enough to fall asleep. He keeps climbing out of bed and calling for attention, his parents become cross, the situation escalates, and the parents eventually give in and allow him to stay up. His difficult bedtime behaviour has been reinforced. He has learned that difficult behaviour gets results: cuddles, drinks, attention, and postponement of bedtime.

He has learned that difficult behaviour gets results!

Sometimes parents are unaware of the importance of limit setting, but sometimes they are well aware that they are failing to set limits. They are unwilling to do so because they know that setting bedtime limits will bring about displays of difficult and disruptive bedtime behaviour. They too have learned that behaviours have consequences! In describing this condition I do not wish to imply that it is the parents' fault that their child has developed a sleep problem or that the difficulties are due to poor parenting. Problems with limit setting often develop when parents have relaxed their usual bedtime rules for some reason, perhaps because the child has been ill. The child enjoys the extra attention that he has been getting and wants it to continue when he is well again. When parents try to bring bedtime back under control he will fight very hard to keep things as they are with all the weapons that he has to hand — tears, screaming, and temper tantrums.

Some children may never have developed regular settling and waking patterns. Children differ markedly in their ability to do this. Some children sleep well from birth, while others seem to be more susceptible to sleep disruption and any changes in routine caused by holidays, illness, visitors, or family problems may cause their sleep patterns to deteriorate. The daytime behaviour of such children may be harder to manage too. Tired parents find it hard to face the prospect of bedtime battles at the end of the day. It seems easier to give in and let the child stay up. First-time parents or parents of children with disabilities are often very anxious about the child, and this makes them unwilling to be firm. If the child cannot speak or understand language it is difficult for the parent to teach the 'rules' of good bedtime behaviour. However, by letting the child who persistently challenges bedtime limits 'win' because it is easier to give in than to struggle, parents are encouraging their child both to continue to be difficult at bedtime and to behave in a similar manner if she wakes at night too.

Sarah was ten years old. She had no language but used Makaton signs. Sarah had a severe settling problem. When her mother put her to bed this is what happened most nights. Her mother gave her a cuddle, settled her in bed, and went downstairs. About five minutes later Sarah would come downstairs. Her mother would take her back to her bedroom, help her into bed, kiss her and go back downstairs. After a few minutes Sarah would go to the top of the stairs and shout. Her mother would go back upstairs, take her by the hand, put her back into bed and close the door. After a few minutes Sarah would open the bedroom door and shout for her mother. Her mother would go upstairs, lock the bedroom door, and return downstairs. Sarah would get out of bed and jump up and down on the bedroom floor, shouting. Sarah's bedroom is immediately above the living room. Her parents would stand the noise as long as they were able, then her mother would go upstairs and give her a tube of Smarties. Sarah had learned that persistent disruptive bedtime behaviour would 'earn' her a tube of Smarties. Her difficult behaviour was being rewarded.

Sleep Associations

One of the most common causes of children's waking problems is **incorrect sleep associations**. Sleep associations are the conditions your child associates with falling asleep. We learn to fall asleep in a particular way and this learned behaviour is repeated every night. If you have got into a habit of rocking your child to sleep, allowing him to fall asleep downstairs, or lying down on his bed with him, he may not be able to fall asleep without these learned associations. As long as you are prepared to continue with these activities there will be no difficulty in settling your child, though it may badly disrupt your evening. The main problem will start in the night during one of the child's arousals. When your child wakes up in the night and the sleep associations are not present — he is not being rocked, or you are not there — he may be unable to go back to sleep. The problem is not that he wakes but that he cannot go back to sleep again after these normal wakings until the conditions for sleep are re-established. For everyone to get a good night's sleep your child needs to be taught to go to sleep alone, in his own bed, without your presence.

"Why do I have to go to sleep on my own?"

Matthew, a four year old, would not go to bed unless his mother lay down with him. She was unable to leave the bedroom until he had gone to sleep. However quietly she tried to slip away, he would open his eyes and start to cry. The problem was made worse by the fact that Matthew would also wake several times in the night and call for his mother. He would not go back to sleep unless she lay down with him on his bed. His mother became exhausted, and eventually sought our help. Matthew was helped to learn new sleep associations, so that he could go to sleep without his mother's presence. His mother started to get a good night's sleep at last.

Night Feeding/Drinking

Some children wake up many times in the night and cannot return to sleep without a bottle or drink. The problem is a common one and occurs in both bottle fed and breast fed babies. The total amount of fluid consumed may be as much as 32 ounces, and such children can wake up from three to eight times per night and frequently wet the bed or wake up with soaked nappies. There is no physical need for feeding during the night after a child is 6 months old, and it is likely either that he has learned to associate feeding with falling asleep and returning to sleep, that he wakes out of habit because he has come to expect feeding during the night, or that discomfort from a full bladder has caused him to wake. This problem can be solved easily using Programme 15 on page 157.

Parental Expectations

Sometimes parents are unhappy about a child's sleep patterns even though they are perfectly normal. Some parents want to have their evening to themselves, but they do not want to get up early in the morning. The problem starts when you put the child to bed at 6 or 7pm and she wakes at 6 o'clock in the morning. This may be fine for her — she is getting 12 hours' sleep — but it is too early for you. Most healthy children cannot sleep for more than about 12 hours. You cannot expect a child to go to bed early and wake late, and so you must adjust your expectations. The table on page 16 will provide a guide for how much sleep children need at each age. Children vary in how much sleep they need, but you can check your child's sleep requirements by keeping a sleep diary for a week and seeing how long your child sleeps if she is undisturbed. Then you may have to adjust your own schedules a little.

Monica and Peter consulted us about their first child, Susan, who was three years old. They liked to have her in bed by six o'clock so that they could watch the evening news on television. However, they were not very happy that she woke well before seven in the morning, alert and ready to play. When they looked at her sleep chart and compared it with average sleep times for children of her age they realised that they were expecting her to sleep for too long. They agreed to put Susan to bed an hour later and she began to wake up about an hour later too.

Disturbances of Sleep Rhythms

Circadian rhythms are biological cycles that repeat about every 24 hours. They include patterns of sleeping, waking, activity, rest, and eating. People's ability to fall asleep and remain asleep is closely linked to the timing of this biological clock, which is automatically reset each day by the use of cues such as meal times, bedtime, and waking time. If these signals were not used, our cycles would operate on a 25-hour day. Adults placed in a dark environment such as a cave with no clocks gradually readjust to a 25-hour cycle.

There are a number of ways in which body rhythms can become irregular and disturb sleep. The best known of these is jet lag, which occurs when a person travels rapidly to a new time zone. Symptoms consist of daytime sleepiness, difficulty in going to sleep and staying asleep, and sometimes stomach upsets. Jet lag usually disappears in a day or two. Shift work can produce similar symptoms. Sleep rhythms become irregular, and workers find it difficult to go to sleep at the necessary times.

Sleep problems in children sometimes arise when their circadian rhythms become disturbed. If this happens, the child may develop **irregular sleep-wake patterns**, or he may develop a sleep pattern that is regular but inappropriate. Children who have developed an **early sleep phase** go to bed early and settle easily, but are awake very early in the morning, whilst those with a **late sleep phase** are not ready for sleep until late in the evening, but then sleep well and have difficulty waking in the morning. Another problem, found most commonly in adolescence, is **insufficient sleep**. This occurs when a young person allows his sleep routines to become disorganised so that he regularly fails to get enough sleep, resulting in excessive daytime sleepiness. If your child has a sleep rhythm disturbance it will not be sufficient to set firm bedtime limits or teach him correct sleep associations. You will need to correct his sleep schedule as well, by resetting his biological clock. Programmes provided in Part IV will show you how to do this.

Four year old Lucy was very difficult to settle at night. Her parents had to fight to get her to go to bed each night, and even when in bed she did not go to sleep until nearly ten o'clock. In the morning she was difficult to wake and very sleepy throughout the day, and she would fall asleep at nursery school. A sleep diary showed that Lucy's sleep was normal, but occurred at the wrong time. Her sleep phase had shifted by about three hours. Her parents carried out a programme to 'reset' her biological clock, and Lucy's sleep cycle was repositioned to a more appropriate time.

The Stressed or Anxious Child

Anxieties and night-time fears are common in children and often cause sleep problems. The child is afraid to go to bed, or wakes in the night frightened and anxious. Sometimes, if the fears are very persistent, it is necessary for the child to see a psychologist who can assess the problem and plan appropriate treatment, but in most cases if you reassure your child at bedtime he will work through his fears and sleep will return to normal. However, settling or waking problems initially caused by night-time fears can quickly become habitual. The child learns to associate difficult bedtime behaviour with extra attention and cuddles.

Another cause of sleep problems in children is **difficulty adjusting to stress**. Episodes of difficult bedtime behaviour can be triggered by any stressful event such as the death of a family member, family breakdown, or even moving house. These problems may only last for a short time, but they can easily become habitual if they are not managed carefully. Juan's mother sought help with the following problem.

My husband and I separated just before Juan's fourth birthday. When his father left, Juan became incontinent for about a year. He has never slept through the night. He is nervous of being alone. I have to sit with him till he goes to sleep. If I move he just follows me as if he were attached to me by a piece of string. He says he is too scared to be alone.

This child had been badly affected by his parents' separation and by the quarrelling and hostility that preceded it. He had become frightened and insecure. Programmes 13 and 14 show you how to deal with a problem like this.

Settling problems, early waking, and waking at night have all been found in children suffering from clinical depression. In these cases when the depression is treated successfully the sleep problem usually clears up. Studies have also found that children of mothers who suffer from depression or psychiatric illness are more likely to develop sleep problems. This may be in part because depressed parents may inadvertently give less attention to their child, causing him anxiety and unhappiness, which in turn affects his sleep. Children are extremely sensitive to their parents' mood and changes in the way they are cared for, especially when they are very young.

Medical Conditions

Any acute illness, particularly when it is accompanied by pain, discomfort or fever, can disrupt a child's sleep patterns temporarily. There are many medical conditions that may result in the child sleeping badly at night. If your child has been ill for a long time or has been in hospital, she may have become anxious and fearful, and this can complicate matters. It is very hard to set firm limits for a chronically sick and fearful child. You may have to take things more slowly, and it will take time and patience to improve your child's sleep.

In any case, it is a good idea to check your child's general health before beginning a sleep programme. Frequently, for example, sleep disturbance in a child who previously slept well may be the only symptom of a middle ear infection, which needs prompt medical attention. **Obstructive sleep apnoea**, a rare disorder characterised by very loud, rasping snoring, restless sleep, and excessive daytime sleepiness, also needs medical attention. Occasionally babies suffer from **food allergies** which may affect their sleep. The discomfort caused by colic and teething may temporarily disrupt sleep in babies. However, teething pains do not cause sleep problems that go on for many weeks, as some parents believe, and **colic** usually resolves by four months of age. In these cases sleep problems originally caused by discomfort or illness can easily become habitual. For a discussion of teething pains and middle ear infection, turn to page 215.

Chronic Illness

Any chronic illness may contribute to a child developing persistent sleep problems. These may be directly caused by the illness or may be associated with anxiety or medication prescribed for the condition. Sometimes it is difficult to work out which factors relating to the illness are causing the sleep problems. Is it caused by the illness itself, its symptoms, the side effects of medication, or the family or child's reaction to the illness? Treatment must be based on management of the illness itself and attention to sleep hygiene. Behavioural programmes such as those found in this book are often helpful in establishing and maintaining more regular sleep patterns.

Hyperactivity

Night waking and restless sleep are frequently reported by parents of children with hyperactivity (attention deficit hyperactivity disorder). A study of hyperactive children reported night wakings in 40% of them. Hyperactivity is thought to be a symptom of a group of disorders with various causes, of which increased daytime activity and disordered sleep are symptoms. For example, children with obstructive sleep apnoea show similar daytime symptoms to hyperactive children. Attention span problems may be a result of poor sleep at night, which produces a tendency for the child to fall asleep suddenly for short periods during the day. It is difficult to tell whether poor sleep is caused by hyperactivity or actually itself causes hyperactivity. If you think your child suffers from hyperactivity you should consult your doctor. When the child's daytime symptoms are controlled, sleep problems tend to improve too. Careful attention to sleep hygiene will help to keep the child's sleep schedule more regular.

Epilepsy in Sleep

Many forms of epilepsy have a clear relationship with sleep. Seizures can occur throughout sleep but are most common during the first two hours of slow wave (Stage IV) sleep, during lighter sleep (Stages I and II) towards the end of the sleep period, or within the first hour after waking. Epilepsy can often be mistaken for parasomnias — sleepwalking, sleep terrors, or nightmares. For example, one form of epilepsy is often mistaken for nightmares until it is realised that the seizures occur several times a night and have a very abrupt onset and end, lasting less than one minute. It is therefore very important that a detailed clinical assessment of a child should be carried out if either epilepsy or a parasomnia is suspected.

Medication

Almost any medication may cause settling and waking problems. In particular, sleep medication is sometimes prescribed inappropriately for children, and can make the problem worse. A study carried out in 1985, for example, found only a slight and short-lived improvement in 1-2 year olds with sleep problems who were prescribed sleep medication. Behavioural techniques and attention to sleep hygiene are much more likely to resolve sleep problems without the risk of side effects.

The most commonly prescribed sleep medications for children are antihistamines (which may cause sleeplessness), sedatives such as chloral hydrate or phenobarbital (which sometimes cause hyperactivity), and short acting benzodiazapines. All these medications may impair the child's daytime functioning. Children may feel drowsy and find it hard to concentrate. Some children exhibit quite severe side-effects, becoming irritable, overactive, aggressive, or poorly coordinated. This has led some experts to say that sleep medication should not be used for children. My own view is that sleep medication may be used to give parents a few nights' sleep when they are close to nervous exhaustion, so that they can recharge their batteries, or it may be used for a few nights at the start of a behavioural programme. It should not be used for long periods without attempting to introduce a sleep programme, since once the drug is withdrawn the poor sleep habits will remain.

Another common medication that sometimes affects sleep is antibiotics, particularly those in liquid suspensions. It is thought to be the suspension that is responsible rather than the antibiotic. Various medications for colds that can be bought over the counter may also affect sleep. If you think that a medication your child is being prescribed may be affecting his sleep patterns, consult your doctor. It may be possible to change the dosage or when it is given, or to switch to a similar medication.

Neurological Problems/Brain Damage

Children who suffer from obvious damage to the neurological system such as that found in cerebral palsy often wake at night or suffer from disturbances of sleep rhythms. It is thought that this may be due to irritation in the brain or some damage to the brain mechanisms that control sleep rhythms and the acts of falling asleep and staying asleep. Most of these children will have a very obvious impairment. Often they will have learning disabilities and they may also have seizures or be blind or deaf.

Sleep problems in children with neurological problems may have a number of causes. It is important to consider carefully all possible factors that may result in poor sleep, rather than assuming that the child's sleep problem is caused by the neurological damage. Keeping a sleep diary is important in evaluating the problem. Sometimes medications such as those used to control epilepsy may be responsible for sleeplessness and administering them at a different time of the day may solve the problem. Sometimes children suffer from seizures during the night. Quite often, however, sleep problems in such children are caused by behavioural factors and can be significantly improved by behavioural methods. Parents we have worked with have found that using a behavioural programme rapidly improves sleep patterns in almost all children. However, the treatment programme must be conducted more slowly than it would be with a child without neurological impairment.

Even if the underlying disorder is considered to be the cause of sleep problems and your doctor prescribes medication to try to make the child's sleep-wake cycle more regular, it is important to follow the principles of sleep hygiene given on page 26 so that the child can be taught not to disturb you during the night. You can use sleep programmes in conjunction with the medication to establish better sleep patterns. However, make sure that you inform your doctor.

Anthony was a three-year-old boy with mild cerebral palsy. He was able to walk, but as yet had no bladder or bowel control. He was able to feed, wash and dress himself with a little help. His hearing and communication skills were poor; he was able to make a few sounds and gestures and to understand a few simple commands. He was very active but had poor concentration. Anthony had never learnt to settle to sleep alone and he woke two or three times each night. His father usually got into bed with him and generally spent much of the night with him. We worked with Anthony's parents to teach him new sleep associations, so that when he woke at night he was able to go back to sleep without disturbing them.

Learning Disability

Children with learning disabilities are considerably more prone to settling and waking problems than other children. The causes are unclear but may lie either in some form of organic brain damage or in the difficulties parents have in teaching appropriate bedtime behaviour to children with poor use and understanding of language. Difficult bedtime behaviour can also be a useful way of gaining attention for a non-speaking child. Such children often use crying as a way of 'punishing' the parent who ignores them when they wake, and this quickly weakens the parent's resolve.

Almost all the parents in our study of children with learning disabilities found behavioural methods of solving sleep problems very effective. These methods are particularly valuable because they do not rely on the child's being able to understand and use speech. Once the children achieved more regular sleep patterns their daytime behaviour improved too. They became less dependent and easier to manage, and had fewer temper tantrums, fewer fights with brothers and sisters, and better concentration.

Events that Disrupt Sleep — The Parasomnias

The parasomnias are a group of disturbances of sleep that interrupt normal sleep patterns. They include sleep terrors, sleepwalking, and sleeptalking. Although each is a separate sleep problem, they have characteristics in common. They often have clear and dramatic symptoms (eg headbanging, tooth grinding). They occur frequently in children and are more common in boys than in girls. The causes are unknown, but it is likely that they are connected with neurological development. Symptoms may range from a single episode to nightly events that continue over a long period of time.

Certain parasomnias, such as nightmares and sleep starts are found in almost all children at some time, while others are more unusual. **Headbanging** (rhythmic movement of the head during sleep), **sleep starts**, and **sleep talking** occur mainly during transitions from wakefulness to sleep, from sleep to wakefulness, or from one sleep stage to another. **Sleepwalking**, **confusional arousals**, and **sleep terrors** are all problems of partial waking that occur during slow-wave (Stage III or IV) sleep. They are associated with confusion and disorientation and cannot be remembered by the child the following day. During confusional arousals the child is neither awake nor asleep — he is able to speak and move about but is not aware of his surroundings. Sleep terrors are often mistaken for nightmares, but differ from them in that the child cannot be comforted by his parents and has no memory of the event afterwards. **Nightmares** occur during REM sleep. Other parasomnias include **sleep bruxism** — tooth grinding during sleep — and **sleep enuresis**, or bedwetting.

The majority of parasomnias disappear on their own as the child gets older, and it is simply necessary to ensure that the child comes to no harm during the episodes. Sleep enuresis can be treated using Programmes 28 and 29 on pages 209 and 210.

Sleep Problems — An Overview

By now I expect is has become clear that while sleep itself is a mysterious process, parts of which are not well understood, the habits that children present around sleep are largely learned. They are shaped by culture, custom, and parental expectations. Many sleep problems, with the exception of the parasomnias, result from difficulties children experience with achieving a regular sleep-wake cycle or from difficulties parents experience in handling potentially short-term disturbances of sleep which quickly become habitual.

Many sleep problems are the result of faulty learning, and behavioural methods of resolving the problems are very effective. However, in some situations the bodily mechanisms that control sleep can become disordered. In these cases it will not be enough to correct the child's sleep habits — his biological clock will need to be reset. If the problem is a genuine disturbance of the sleep-wake cycle it will then resolve. If it persists, however, it is more likely that it is a disturbance of habit, and you will have to use behavioural techniques to resolve it.

Sometimes self-help methods you will read concentrate only on teaching parents behavioural methods of solving sleep problems. In this book we combine behavioural techniques with an understanding of sleep problems and processes. Sometimes the child's sleep clock may have to be reset, or he may have to learn new conditions to associate with falling asleep. You may have to learn how to set appropriate limits for his bedtime behaviour, and you may have to encourage his cooperation by using incentives. Even though your child seems more prone to disturbances of sleep rhythm, or you have considered him to be a naturally poor sleeper, you will find that his sleep problems will improve considerably once you make the appropriate changes in his routines, schedules, sleep environment, or the way you handle bedtime.

Being involved in solving your child's sleep problem will make you feel rightly that you are in control. You are not helpless — you are doing something to deal with the problem. Once you understand the reasons for your child's poor sleep you may find it very simple to put things right. The cure will come simply and quickly. Sometimes, though, you may have to try more than one programme until you find what works for you and your child. The important thing is to keep working at it until you succeed.

A very few children sleep poorly for reasons that doctors cannot yet identify. For these, this guide may help very little. However, it is very unlikely that your child is one of these poor sleepers. Cases of children with genuine inability to sleep are very rare indeed. Almost certainly your child's sleep problem can be improved.

"She cannot be serious!"

CHAPTER 4

TAKING A SLEEP HISTORY

The previous chapter looked at the different causes of sleep problems in children. Answering the following questions on your child's sleep history will help to you to get a clearer idea of the kind of problem that is affecting your own child.

MY CHILD'S SLEEP HISTORY

1. When did the problem start? Has it existed since birth or did it start after a significant event such as illness or moving house?

This question assesses how long the problem has been going on and whether it may have been initially triggered by a stressful event.

2. What time does your child normally go to bed and get up?

3. Does he usually keep to a regular schedule?

These questions assess the regularity of your child's sleep-wake pattern. Most children's bedtime and waking time do not vary by more than about an hour from day to day. If your child's schedule varies more, this may be part of the problem and you will need to concentrate on setting a more regular schedule.

4. What activities does your child do in the hour before bedtime?

If your child is very active in the hour before bedtime you might try carrying out a more relaxing routine during this time to allow him to wind down and prepare for bed.

5. Does your child have a regular bedtime routine? If yes, how long does this last?

If your child does not have a routine it's a good idea to start one immediately, to teach him to anticipate and prepare for bedtime.

6. How long does it normally take your child to fall asleep/settle?

This question assesses sleep latency, which means how long it takes your child to fall asleep from going to bed to the beginning of sleep.

7. Does he have trouble settling to sleep? If it takes longer than half an hour for your child to fall asleep, what does he do during that time?

8. What do you (and your partner) do in response to settling problems?

These questions assess your child's settling problems. If he engages in bedtime battles until you usually give in and let him stay up you may have to make some changes in the way you handle bedtime. You may be unintentionally rewarding his difficult bedtime behaviour.

9. Does your child fall asleep somewhere other than in his own bedroom? If so, where?

10. Has your child ever learned to go to sleep alone?

11. What associations does your child require to fall asleep? (eg parent lying on bed, being rocked or held, special toy or teddy, dummy, bottle, sofa, night light, television on, etc)

These questions consider your child's sleep associations. If your child learns to associate going to sleep with the presence of certain conditions — being downstairs, being rocked or cuddled, or having you lie down with him, being in your bed, or sucking a dummy — he will only be unable to go back to sleep when he wakes if these conditions are present, and he will probably wake you up by crying or calling for attention. You will need to teach him new sleep associations so he learns to fall asleep alone in his own bed.

12. Does your child express fears about going to sleep? What are they? Is he afraid of the dark?

Some children have fears at night which make it difficult for them to settle to sleep. They may be worrying about stressful events that have occured in the family, or they may simply have fears triggered by watching an exciting film on television or reading a particularly vivid story. Some children may be afraid of the dark. You may find it helpful to teach the child relaxation exercises to help him fall asleep more easily (see Programme 14 on page 152) or to use Programme 11 or 12 on pages 142 and 143. A night light may be used for a child who is afraid of the dark.

13. After your child has gone to sleep does he wake up again? How many times per night? How many nights per week? How long is each awakening? What does he do?

14. If your child wakes at night do you have to carry out certain practices/ activities to get him to fall asleep again?

These questions assess your child's behaviour when he wakes at night. Most children wake from 5 to 15 times each night but are able to go back to sleep within a few seconds and may not even remember waking. Usually the problem is not with waking but with what happens next. If you keep attending to your child when he wakes he will soon get into the habit of calling for you every time he wakes. His difficult behaviour is being reinforced. You can resolve this by using a graded steps programme at night when he wakes. You may first have to teach him new sleep associations so that he can go back to sleep without your presence. This will involve teaching him to fall asleep alone in his own bed.

15. Do you still give your child drinks or a bottle during the night?

This question assesses whether night feeding could be the problem.

16. Does your child exhibit any unusual behaviours or movements during sleep? Does your child walk in his sleep? talk in his sleep? bang his head or body rock? wake suddenly with a piercing scream? jerk his legs? grind his teeth? wet the bed? have frightening dreams?

This question will tell you whether your child is suffering from one of the parasomnias, such as nightmares, sleep terrors, sleep talking or sleep walking. Information about these problems can be found in Part IV.

17. Does your child snore very loudly during sleep?

If your child snores very loudly during sleep and seems to stop breathing for periods of 20 seconds, starting again with a rasping snort, he may be suffering from obstructive sleep apnoea. You should consult your doctor as soon as possible.

18. What time does your child wake in the morning? Does he wake unusually early? Does he wake spontaneously or do you have to wake him? Is it difficult to wake him? How does he feel on waking — tired, bad tempered, happy?

This question assesses whether your child's sleep phase may have shifted. If your child is difficult to get to sleep at night and is difficult to wake in the morning and sleepy during the day, he may have developed a late sleep phase. If he goes to sleep and wakes unusually early he may have developed an early sleep phase. In both cases you will need to reset his biological clock.

19. Is your child unusually sleepy during the day?

The most common cause of excessive daytime sleepiness is obstructive sleep apnoea. If your child does not snore loudly at night and does not suffer from a clear medical or neurological disorder, sleepiness in the daytime may be due to a late sleep phase or late bedtimes. In these cases, daytime sleepiness, while present, is not excessive. In adolescence, excessive sleepiness may be due to insufficient sleep and you may have to adjust the amount of time your child stays in bed until his daytime sleepiness disappears.

20. Does your child have naps during the day? How many? For how long?

This question assesses your child's sleep-wake pattern. If he sleeps frequently during the day you may find that cutting out the naps improves his sleep. If cutting the naps is unsuccessful he may have developed an irregular sleep-wake pattern and you will have to help him to make it more regular.

21. What is the child's total sleep time? How does this compare with average sleep times for children of the same age shown on page 16?

Some children need more sleep, others less, so the average sleep time chart on page 16 can only be used as a rough guide. If your child sleeps less than the average child but does not appear sleepy during the day and functions well, you have no need to worry, but if your child is awake for long periods at night and is fractious and sleepy during the day, then he has a sleep problem. This question, along with Question 2, will give an indication of the efficiency of your child's sleep pattern — e.g. if he stays in the bed for 8 hours but sleep only 6 hours his sleep efficiency is only 75%. The less efficient your child's sleep, the more severe is his sleep problem.

An Example

Here is Jill's history. Jill, aged 6, has been disturbing her parents, waking and crying in the night. Examining her sleep history will show you how it helps in the analysis of Jill's sleep problem.

JILL'S SLEEP HISTORY

1. When did the problem start? Has it existed since birth or did it start after a significant event such as illness or moving house?

   From birth

2. What time does your child normally go to bed and get up?

   7.30 pm/8.00 pm

3. Does she usually keep to a regular schedule?

   Yes

4. What activities does your child do in the hour before bedtime?

   Plays quietly

5. Does your child have a regular bedtime routine? If yes, how long does this last?

   Yes. Half an hour

6. How long does it normally take your child to fall asleep/settle?

   About 20 minutes

7. Does she have trouble settling to sleep? If it takes longer than half an hour for your child to fall asleep, what does she do during that time?

   No problems as long as I lie down with her

8. What do you (and your partner) do in response to settling problems?

   N/A

9. Has your child ever learned to sleep alone?

   No

10. Does your child fall asleep somewhere other than in her own bedroom? If so, where?

    No

11. What associations does your child require to fall asleep? (eg parent lying on bed, being rocked or held, special toy or teddy, dummy, bottle, sofa, night light, television on, etc)

    I lie down with her until she falls asleep

12. Does your child express fears about going to sleep? What are they? Is she afraid of the dark?

    No

13. After your child has gone to sleep does she wake up again? How many times per night? How many nights per week? How long is each awakening? What does she do?

    Yes. About twice every night, for 20-30 minutes. Wakes and cries.

14. If your child wakes at night do you have to carry out certain practices/ activities to get her to fall asleep again?

    Yes, I lie down with her or let her come into our bed

15. Do you still give your child drinks or a bottle during the night?

    No

16. Does your child exhibit any unusual behaviours or movements during sleep? Does your child walk in her sleep? talk in her sleep? bang her head or body rock? wake suddenly with a piercing scream? jerk her legs? grind her teeth? wet the bed? have frightening dreams?

    No

17. Does your child snore very loudly during sleep?

    No

18. What time does your child wake in the morning? Does she wake unusually early? Does she wake spontaneously or do you have to wake her? Is it difficult to wake her? How does she feel on waking — tired, bad tempered, happy?

    7.30, spontaneously, usually happy

19. Is your child unusually sleepy during the day?

    No

20. Does your child have naps during the day? How many? For how long?

    No

21. What is the child's total sleep time? How does this compare with average sleep times for children of the same age shown on page 16?

    11 hours. Appropriate for her age

The sleep history shows that Jill has incorrect sleep associations. She does not have a problem falling asleep because the conditions she associates with falling asleep are present — her mother lies down with her. However, when she wakes up in the night the conditions she associates with falling asleep are not present. She cannot go back to sleep without those cues or associations, and so she disturbs her parents by crying and calling for attention. When this happens, Jill's mother reinforces her undesired behaviour by attending to her needs, finally lying down on her bed to get her back to sleep, or allowing her to come into her parents' bed. This makes it more likely that she will repeat the behaviour when similar circumstances occur. Jill's problems can be resolved by following a step-by-step programme that will teach her new sleep associations and will reinforce her new appropriate night-time behaviour.

The next part of this book will help you to understand how your own child's difficult night-time behaviour is being maintained and will teach you methods for changing it.

PART II

HOW TO CHANGE YOUR CHILD'S NIGHT-TIME BEHAVIOUR

Chapter 1

Analysing Your Child's Behaviour

The methods we have developed to resolve sleep problems work well and are suitable for all children. The approach we use is based on theories of how people learn. It is known as the behavioural approach. The behavioural approach offers a method you can use to encourage your child to behave more acceptably at night-time. It is not a magical cure. It will require both your child and you to make changes in your behaviour and responses to each other. You will need to work hard at it and to be firm and consistent. The behavioural approach is based on well researched principles. In this book we will teach you how to use these principles to improve the difficult sleep patterns of your child and to feel more confident in your ability to deal with night-time disturbance in the future. You may think that you have tried some of these methods in the past and found they did not work. However, perhaps you did not carry them out in precisely the way we are going to suggest, so please give them a chance.

The approach will show you how to teach your child desirable behaviour and how to help him unlearn the difficult behaviour he has picked up along the way. It will also show you how to help the child maintain the new behaviour once he has learned it. The approach does not concern itself with the origins of the child's problems, which may be difficult or impossible to determine, but takes the optimistic view that whatever the original cause, the behaviour is now being partly or wholly maintained or kept going by current circumstances which can be changed. This means that you, the parents, have an important role to play in shaping your child's behaviour.

The approach focuses on what you can observe in your child's behaviour, rather than what he may be thinking or feeling. This is particularly helpful when the child has a physical or mental disability because such children are often unable to communicate what is going on inside them and have to rely on their parents to discover what their needs and wishes are. The behavioural approach will also help you to sort out and simplify the messages given to your child so that he has a better chance of understanding.

What do we mean by the term *behaviour*? Often when people use the word behaviour they also use the words 'good' or 'bad'. In the behavioural model the word behaviour refers to everything we do. Any single observable action is a behaviour. We are behaving all the time. Eating, smiling, talking, shouting, jumping, crying are all behaviours. From a behavioural perspective, the things that your child does when he is put to bed, or when he wakes in the night are seen as behaviours that he *actively chooses* from a range of possible responses. Night-time behaviour, whether it is desirable or problem behaviour, is a *learned habit*. A child who has learned difficult night-time behaviour can also learn not to engage in it, and to engage in appropriate night-time behaviour instead. The learning is brought about by analysing the child's behaviour and than making carefully planned changes in his environment.

Understanding Difficult Night-time Behaviour: The ABC Analysis

Research shows that to understand what makes difficult night-time behaviour continue you must look carefully at the behaviour and at what happens immediately before and immediately after it occurs. This is known as the ABC of behaviour.

ANTECEDENT ⇨	BEHAVIOUR ⇨	CONSEQUENCES
What leads up to (triggers) the behaviour.	What the child says and does.	What happens immediately after the behaviour that encourages the child to behave in a similar or different way next time.

The A stands for Antecedents — what happens immediately before the behaviour which acts as a trigger for that behaviour? Does putting your child to bed set the problem off? Or telling him that it's time for bed? Or does the simple act of waking in the night seem to trigger his behaviour? The B is the Behaviour itself — what exactly is the night-time behaviour causing concern? The C stands for Consequences — what follows or happens as a result of a display of difficult night-time behaviour?

B is for Behaviour

Defining the Sleep Problem

To carry out an ABC analysis we start with the behaviour. If you want to change someone's behaviour, you must be clear about the specific problem that you want to change and what change you would like to see. Consider your child's night-time behaviour. What precisely is he doing wrong? Psychologists call the behaviour you want to change the **problem behaviour**. If your answer is fuzzy, eg 'Pat is always difficult at bedtime', it is difficult to plan a strategy for change. If your answer is specific, 'Sally gets out of bed when she wakes up and comes into our bedroom', then an effective strategy for changing the behaviour can be planned. The new behaviour you would like to see instead is called the target behaviour. If Tom keeps coming downstairs after being put to bed at night, coming downstairs after bedtime would be Tom's problem behaviour. His parents would be able to say that the **target behaviour** would be for Tom to stay in his own bed and settle quietly to sleep. Another example of a problem behaviour is when a child wakes up and cries three or four times in the night. The problem behaviour is the child's crying. The target behaviour would be for the child not to disturb his parents when he wakes. If the child is presenting more than one difficult behaviour, you will have to decide which is causing you the most difficulty. You can then work on that problem and deal with the other problems later.

It is important to work out why a behaviour is being identified as a problem. Sometimes there is more than one reason. Disrupted sleep may interfere with the needs of your child, resulting in tiredness and bad temper the next day, or it can interfere with your own sleep or disrupt your evening. Sometimes it may disturb the sleep of brothers and sisters. You should be clear about what the sleep problem is and why you want to change it. On the next page there is an ABC chart. Fill in the sleep behaviour that you want to change in the Behaviour section. Be as precise as you can. Now write in the behaviour you would like to see in its place. Be clear about what changes you would like to make.

STEP 1

DEFINE THE PROBLEM NIGHT-TIME BEHAVIOURS AND THE BEHAVIOURS THAT SHOULD REPLACE THEM

1. Write down on the ABC chart what it is that your child does at night-time that makes you believe that she has a sleep problem.
2. Write down what you would like her to do at night-time instead.

Measuring How Often the Sleep Problem Occurs

As a first step in using the behavioural approach you have specified the night-time behaviour you wish to change. You also need to make an accurate record of how often it happens. You should already have begun to fill in a sleep diary for one week (see page 7). The sleep diary records how frequently the sleep problem occurs and provides important details that you will need in order to analyse the problem behaviour. You should keep the diary by the bed and fill it in every night. Each time the problem behaviour occurs write a clear description in the diary of the antecedents — what events immediately preceded the problem behaviour — and the consequences — what events occurred immediately afterwards. Don't do anything different from what you have done in the past for this week. We want you to get a

THE ABC CHART

ANTECEDENTS

What antecedent conditions set the behaviour off?

Example: John wakes in the night and finds he is alone

BEHAVIOUR

What is the behaviour that is being complained of? How frequently does it occur?

Example: John wakes up four or five times in the night and disturbs his parents by crying

What behaviour would you like to see in its place?

Example: John will sleep from 8pm to 7am without waking and calling for his parents

CONSEQUENCES

What happens as a result of the display of difficult behaviour?

Example: John's mother goes into his bedroom, gives him a drink, and stays with him until he falls asleep picture of how things are at present. You should continue to keep a record of your child's behaviour once you begin a programme and right through until the end. It will help you to monitor your child's progress and will provide evidence of whether the programme is having an effect on her behaviour. If you do not fill it in regularly each night the programme is unlikely to succeed and you will be unable to check your child's progress. It's easy to forget how bad the problem was once it starts to get better. If you have not already done so, start to fill in the diary for one week NOW.

STEP 2

FILL IN A SLEEP DIARY TO RECORD THE FREQUENCY OF THE PROBLEM NIGHT-TIME BEHAVIOUR FOR ONE WEEK

1. How frequently per night/week does the problem behaviour occur?
2. How long does each episode of problem behaviour last?

C is for Consequences

The consequences are the most important part of the ABC analysis. We therefore deal with the consequences of behaviour before the antecedents. The nature of the consequences — things that happen immediately after a behaviour — helps to shape behaviour by teaching your child whether his behaviour is successful or not. Three kinds of consequences strongly influence the way a child behaves and whether he will repeat a behaviour in the future. These are consequences that are rewarding (strengthening), consequences that are extinguishing (reducing), and consequences that are punishing.

Consequences that are Rewarding

If your child behaves in a particular way and as a result of this behaviour something pleasant happens to her, she will be more likely to repeat the behaviour in the future. Psychologists call this **positive reinforcement**. For example, if your child tidies her room and you praise her clearly for this, she will be more likely to repeat that behaviour another time. So if you say clearly to the child 'Jean, I am very pleased that you have tidied your room', Jean will be more likely to tidy her room again. You can make the consequences of the behaviour rewarding even if your child does not understand language, but you will need to be simpler. If you say, 'Good girl!' and give your child a big hug immediately after she has carried out the behaviour, she will learn to associate your praise with her behaviour.

She will be more likely to behave that way again. Here is an example. Alice has been waking up in the night and crying.

ANTECEDENT ⇨	BEHAVIOUR ⇨	CONSEQUENCES
Alice's mother puts her to bed.	Alice settles and sleeps through the night.	In the morning Alice's mother praises her for sleeping right through.

Alice will be likely to repeat her more acceptable behaviour next time because it has been reinforced. Here are two more examples of positive reinforcement.

- ❖ June's mother gives her a cuddle because she got herself ready for bed.
- ❖ George's father takes him to a football match because he has stayed in his own bed all week.

In these situations a rewarding consequence occurs as a result of the child's desirable night-time behaviour. The behaviour has been positively reinforced.

Sometimes, though, parents unintentionally reinforce undesirable behaviour. Here is an example.

ANTECEDENT ⇨	BEHAVIOUR ⇨	CONSEQUENCES
David's mother put him to bed.	He screamed and cried.	His mother allowed him to come downstairs and watch TV.

In this case David received positive reinforcement for behaving in an undesirable manner. David will be likely to repeat his behaviour because it worked — he was allowed to come downstairs and postpone bedtime. Let us take another example:

ANTECEDENT ⇨	BEHAVIOUR ⇨	CONSEQUENCES
Tom's mother takes him to bed and says "Goodnight"	Tom screams, cries, and comes downstairs.	Tom is given cuddles, drinks, attention, and postponement of bedtime.

What has Tom learned? Tom's display of tantrums and difficult behaviour has been extremely successful. The consequences of his behaviour have been reinforcing — postponement of bedtime, cuddles, drinks, and attention. Tom is likely to display the same behaviour again. In time it will become a learned habit.

Reinforcement can be both positive and negative. Negative reinforcement occurs when behaving in a particular manner avoids an unpleasant outcome/consequence. If, for example, your child behaves in a particular way (settles in bed) to avoid or escape an unpleasant situation (being scolded) you are providing negative reinforcement for her efforts. Eventually a mere warning of a penalty is enough of a reminder. You don't have to apply the penalty because she knows you always keep your word. Examples are:

- ❖ staying in bed to avoid mother's disapproval
- ❖ settling quietly at night to avoid being smacked

In the two examples, behaving acceptably allows the child to avoid an 'unpleasant' consequence.

Both positive and negative reinforcement strengthen behaviour — that is, they encourage the child to repeat the behaviour, and teach her to behave in a certain way. It's easy to confuse them, but if you remember that negative generally means taking something away and positive means presenting or starting something, you will be able to distinguish between them. Negative reinforcement does not mean punishment: it is reinforcement that takes the form of relief from something unpleasant.

Consequences that are Extinguishing

If a child does something but she is not reinforced, or her behaviour is ignored, she will slowly become less likely to repeat that behaviour. The behaviour dies away or is 'extinguished'. Extinguishing consequences reduce behaviour — they make it less likely to happen again. One form of extinction, planned ignoring, can be a useful way of discouraging an undesirable behaviour like night-time crying.

Here is an example. Janice has been used to her mother coming to her at bedtime and staying until she falls asleep.

ANTECEDENT ⇨	BEHAVIOUR ⇨	CONSEQUENCES
Janice's mother settles her in bed and says goodnight.	Janice cries.	Her mother checks that she is okay and ignores the crying.

If Janice's night-time crying is ignored, she may cry harder at first to get her mother to come. When this brings no rewards she will slowly stop doing it, though she will probably get worse before she gets better. Other examples of extinction — ways to arrange things so that the child receives no reinforcement following undesirable behaviour — include taking the child who keeps getting into bed with you straight back to his own bed with as little interaction as possible, and substituting water in a bottle for the child who guzzles juice all night. Both of these involve withholding the reinforcement that has been maintaining a behaviour.

Sometimes parents accidentally overlook or ignore their child's desirable behaviour. Here is an example.

ANTECEDENT ⇨	BEHAVIOUR ⇨	CONSEQUENCES
Johns mother tells him it's bedtime.	John gets himself ready for bed and puts himself to bed.	John's mother carries on watching the television.

John's mother has ignored his desirable behaviour. It won't be surprising if John is difficult about going to bed tomorrow. If John's mother continues to ignore desirable behaviour, she will be in danger of extinguishing the behaviour she wants to encourage.

Consequences that are Punishing

There are also a variety of consequences that children do not find pleasing — things they would rather avoid. If a child does something and as a result of this behaviour something unrewarding happens to him, then he will be less likely to do it again in the future. The behavioural model refers to these consequences as punishers. Like extinguishing consequences, punishers are events that weaken or discourage behaviour — that is, they reduce the likelihood of the behaviour occurring in the future. Being told off, smacked, criticised, shouted at, or isolated can all act as punishers. So can withdrawal of approval or privileges. If when Tom cries in the night, for example, his father goes into his bedroom and smacks him, Tom will be less likely to repeat the behaviour next time. If your child behaves badly at bedtime and you punish him clearly and consistently for this, he is less likely to repeat the behaviour. As with reinforcement, children differ in what they find punishing. Although punishing a child with a quick smack may release some of your frustrations, there is no evidence that it will work very well. Sometimes parents find that they have to make punishments more and more severe to get them to work. For some children, the attention that accompanies the punishment turns it into a reward. Smacking may actually keep the undesired behaviour going. Alternatively it may teach the child to fear and dislike her parents. In this book we are more concerned with reinforcement than with punishment. But it is important to understand the role that punishment can play in shaping behaviour.

Now look at your own child's behaviour in the diary. What follows from a display of difficult behaviour? Did you perhaps go in to her, delay bedtime, provide extra hugs, cuddles, and attention, or allow her to sleep in your bed? If you did any of these things you will have encouraged her to behave that way next time she goes to bed or wakes in the night. Write down the consequences of your child's night-time behaviour in the Consequences section of the ABC chart.

STEP 3

FILL IN THE CONSEQUENCES SECTION OF THE ABC CHART

What happens immediately after the behaviour that encourages your child to behave in a similar way next time?

A is for Antecedents

The antecedents of behaviour — the cues or triggers that set the behaviour off — are an important part of the ABC analysis. As parents you will know that particular situations seem to trigger difficult behaviour. If your child is very tired, for example, or feeling unwell, when you ask him to do something he does not want to, or when you are busy doing something else — perhaps attending to a brother or sister — your child will start to behave badly. Some children seem to show their worst side when there are other people around — grandparents, for example. Some behave perfectly well if their father is present, but turn into little horrors when their mother is alone with them. With bedtime problems the trigger for the difficult behaviour is usually a demand placed upon the child — to go to bed. Children who have been behaving quite reasonably until then suddenly start to whine and cry and pester for attention. They may try to wheedle for 'just one more story' or ask you to lie down on the bed with them. They may come downstairs or shout from the bedroom. They may stay in their room but create chaos, taking things out of drawers and throwing toys about. However, if they are away from home, staying with a favourite aunt, for example, they may behave like little angels, settling quickly and quietly when put to bed. Children tailor their behaviour to the situation they find themselves in. They look around, consider the rules, the firmness of the adult, and what is expected of them, and adapt their behaviour accordingly.

Another kind of antecedent to difficult night-time behaviour happens when the child who has been rocked to sleep, or has had his mother lie down with him until he falls asleep, suddenly wakes up to find there is no-one there. Look at this example.

Jane's mother usually persuades her to settle to sleep at night by lying down beside her until she falls asleep. When Jane wakes up in the night to find her mother is absent she cries and goes into her parents' bedroom and gets into her parents' bed. Her mother allows her to stay there.

What has Jane learned? She seems to have learned to associate going to sleep with her mother's comforting presence. When she wakes in the night, however, she is unable to go back to sleep because these associations are not present. Her response to this is to go into her parents' room and get into bed. When she is allowed to stay she learns that crying exerts control over her surroundings. She got her mother's attention and was allowed to stay in her parents' bed. Would she do it again?

ANTECEDENT ⇨	**BEHAVIOUR** ⇨	**CONSEQUENCES**
What sets the difficult night-time behaviour off?	*What is the behaviour?*	*What consequences flow from a display of difficult night-time behaviour?*
Jane's mother lies down on the bed until Jane falls asleep.	Jane settles.	The parents' evening is peaceful.
Jane wakes up in the night to find no-one is there.	Jane cries and goes into her parents' room and bed.	Jane is allowed to stay in her parents' bed. Parents' and child's sleep is disrupted.

Think about your own child's sleep problem and look at the diary you have filled in. What seems to trigger your child's display of difficult night-time behaviour? Write this down in the Antecedents section of the ABC chart. Does the simple act of putting her to bed trigger the difficult behaviour? Or do you lie down with her while she falls asleep? If you do this, problems may start when she wakes in the night to find herself alone.

STEP 4

FILL IN THE ANTECEDENTS SECTION OF THE ABC CHART

What leads up to (triggers) the behaviour?

If you know the situations that are likely to trigger difficult night-time behaviour, there are things you can do to anticipate trouble and to avoid it. If, for example, your child cries and refuses to go to bed when bedtime arrives, you can set up a relaxing bedtime routine which will let your child know that bedtime is approaching and give her time to get used to the idea. If your child understands language, you can warn her beforehand that however much fuss she makes you will not give in, but if she settles quietly you will read her a bedtime story.

You must make these messages clear and always be consistent. Don't postpone bedtime one night but try to enforce it the next. Your child must learn the rules of desirable night-time behaviour. Make sure that you and your partner are in agreement about what those rules should be. Children soon learn to play off one parent against another if they sense that one will give in more easily. You should also make sure that the child is listening to what you say. Don't tell her while she is watching TV or playing with her toys. You should state the rules in a clear, confident, she-who-must-be-obeyed way. If you've been ground down by months of late bedtimes and tantrums, practise doing this alone until you feel more confident.

STEP 5

EXAMINE THE ABC CHART THAT YOU HAVE FILLED IN

A What sets the behaviour off?

B What is the behaviour you are complaining of?

C What consequences follow from the behaviour? What is the 'pay-off' for the child?

Consolidating Learning

Analysing your child's night-time behaviour will help you to understand that frequently difficult night-time behaviours have become habitual because they have been rewarded or reinforced in the past and continue to be rewarded. As we have said, reinforcers are consequences that make similar behaviour more likely to occur. So given a particular antecedent — say putting your child to bed at night — difficult behaviour that has been and continues to be reinforced will be more likely to occur. In the end, every time you put the child to bed the behaviour will occur. The child has learned to behave in a certain way. The antecedent — putting the child to bed — is seen as causing the behaviour.

Let us look at an example. John refuses to settle, screams, and cries when his mother puts him to bed. Putting John to bed is the clear trigger for this behaviour. In terms of our ABC analysis, however, the explanation is not a complete one. The reason John responds with screams and cries when his mother puts him to bed is that screaming and crying at bedtimes in the past has brought reinforcing consequences. Putting John to bed triggers his crying fits because it also signals the coming of the reinforcement — his mother lying down with him and cuddling him until he falls asleep. John has learned that he can avoid the boring situation of being left to go to sleep alone and ensure his mother stays with him until he falls asleep by making a fuss at bedtime. Perhaps sometimes John's mother will not give in immediately — perhaps she will get cross, tell him off, and leave the bedroom. However, as long as she does give in in the end, John will have got what he wants. He may have to make a bigger fuss and tolerate his mother's irritation, but the reinforcement of her staying with him until he sleeps is a greater incentive, and he has learned that his mother *always gives in in the end*.

Just as a consistent pattern of reinforcement causes a child to learn to behave in a certain way, so does extinction or a consistent pattern of punishment. Both extinction and punishment make a behaviour less likely to occur. If when a child cries for his parents in the night he is ignored or punished, then eventually he will stop crying at night. We can say that the child has learned not to do the behaviour. Punishment is certainly not a method we want to encourage in this book, but it is worth explaining to ensure an understanding of behavioural principles.

Points to Remember

Night-time behaviour is maintained by its consequences.

- Night-time behaviour that is followed by a reinforcing consequence will continue.
- Night-time behaviour that is followed by a punishing consequence will decrease.
- Night-time behaviour that is not reinforced will not continue, but will gradually disappear.

Chapter 2

Four Strategies for Changing Behaviour

Once you understand the behavioural approach you will see that it offers you a number of different strategies for changing your child's difficult night-time behaviour. Four main strategies are suggested in this chapter. The first involves selecting a new, more appropriate night-time behaviour (getting the child to stay in his own bed) to replace an unwanted behaviour (coming downstairs), and establishing consequences for it (attention, reward, praise). Then the child is rewarded consistently whenever he shows the new behaviour. This is called positive reinforcement. The child's behaviour is strengthened by attending to it (noticing it) and by providing immediate, reliable and pleasant consequences. The second strategy involves replacing or changing the antecedents of behaviour. In the case of bedtime behaviour, we can alter the antecedents that trigger bedtime battles by providing systematic reminders — in the form of cues and positive routines — that bedtime is approaching, rather than abruptly taking the child to bed. We call this providing the conditions that encourage sleep. Since behaviour is determined by its consequences as well as its antecedents we can shape bedtime behaviour by changing its consequences too. The third strategy, therefore, involves removing the reinforcer or reward that is maintaining the difficult behaviour. We do this by ignoring or not attending to the behaviour and thus removing the incentive for the child to behave badly. This is called extinction or planned ignoring. The fourth technique is to establish a more gradual programme of change (graduated extinction), which will slowly shape and improve your child's night-time behaviour. It involves removing the particular attention or other reinforcer that is maintaining the child's behaviour, but this is accomplished in a series of gradual steps. Let us look at these methods in greater detail.

1. Positive Reinforcement

A major way of encouraging your child to behave as you want him to is to use positive reinforcement (reward). For example, if you praise your child for trying hard to dress himself, he will be more likely to try hard again. It is the same with night-time behaviour. You can strengthen or encourage an appropriate night-time behaviour by attending to (noticing) it and by providing immediate, reliable and pleasant consequences. Reinforcers/rewards can be anything the child enjoys, such as praise, hugs, sweets, or toys. If your child can understand, you can use a star chart where he is rewarded with a gold star if he stays in bed or sleeps through the night without disturbing you. When a number of stars have been collected they

"Good boy, Tom, for getting ready for bed!"

can be exchanged for a small toy. Positive reinforcement can be used in conjunction with other techniques.

Kinds of Rewards

Reinforcers are what pleases and rewards your child at the time. Not all children find the same rewards pleasing. For example, most children like being praised, but for some children, notably children with autism, social praise is not reinforcing but something to avoid. An alternative reward must be found. Although rewards differ for different children, it is possible to identify certain types. These can be **material** (sweets, small toys, food, drink, books, items for a collection — eg Pokemon cards); **social** (praise, hugs, smiles, attention, time with parents, star charts); **sensory** (a musical toy, a teaspoon of yoghurt, a pretty picture, being touched or stroked, ice cream); or **activity** (being allowed to do a favourite activity, eg playing a game, being taken to the swimming pool, a trip to the park).

How to Choose a Reward

A reward is something that the child finds pleasing and will work for. Sometimes parents say 'My child doesn't find anything rewarding'. This never turns out to be the case. Sometimes you need to use a little imagination to find a suitable reward, but it is always possible to find something that gives your child pleasure. Here are three ways to find out what is rewarding for your child.

The first is experience with the child. Of course if you know your own child well you will know what kind of things he enjoys that may be used as reinforcers. Most children like to please their parents and for these social praise, a hug or cuddle will act as an important reinforcer. Many children like to be given a small toy as a reward. For children with profound handicaps who have not learned to respond to more acceptable reinforcers such as praise, food reinforcement may be very important. A sweet or a spoonful of yoghurt given in the morning after a peaceful night will serve to strengthen the child's behaviour.

Another way to find out what your child finds rewarding is to give him a choice. If your child understands language you can ask him. If he has no language you can put several rewards in front of him and see which he reaches for. If you put two objects in front of a child several times you will find out if one is chosen more frequently.

Lastly, you can test rewards one after the other. Sometimes you cannot put all possible rewards in front of your child at the same time. Social rewards can only be tried out one after the other. Suppose you want to try a cuddle, a sweet, and a musical toy as possible reinforcers. You would offer each a number of times and ask your child which he prefers. If he has no language you must watch him carefully to observe signs of enjoyment such as smiling, attempts to reach the reward, or increased movement. If your child has a physical or mental disability it may be harder to find toys that can act as reinforcers. There is a firm called Toys for the Handicapped, which makes a great many battery operated reward toys. These are particularly easy for disabled children to use. You will find their address on page 203.

Rules for Giving Rewards

There are five basic rules for providing rewards:

Clarity: Make the rules for getting a reward clear and simple.

Immediacy: Reward your child as soon as possible after he has performed the appropriate behaviour. The child should be able to earn a reward easily at first. Later on the requirements for earning a reward can be increased.

Strength: Give the strongest reward possible — ie the one your child likes best.

Attention-getting: Use a reward that gets your child's attention.

Consistency: Reward your child every time he performs the appropriate behaviour until the behaviour is established. You can then reward the child occasionally.

If possible, tell your child what it is he has to do to get a reward. Make any instructions clear and simple. Remember, it is the behaviour that is being praised or rewarded, not the whole child. Make sure you identify the behaviour specifically. For example, you might say 'Good boy, Nicky, for sleeping through the night!', rather than just 'Good boy!'. You can experiment with different ways of giving praise. At first, reward immediately and often. Eventually, when the behaviour is established, you can fade the reward, ie not give it every time the behaviour is carried out successfully. Eventually you can stop giving the reward entirely. Select the reward carefully. Some rewards are stronger than others. Use a variety of rewards and arrange for there to be more than one source of reinforcement — get your child's father or grandparents to offer the reward sometimes if they are present. Make sure they offer the reward promptly when the desired behaviour occurs. Parents' praise is often what makes a reward effective. You should praise your child freely when he has behaved as you want at bedtime. If you feel awkward about praising your child you may need to practise giving praise with warmth and enthusiasm, remembering to make eye contact with him. Don't mix criticism with praise. Reward him for trying as well as for success if the task is hard. Never take away a reward once it has been earned.

Here is a programme where positive reinforcement was used. Carl's programme combined extinction and positive reinforcement. He was also given lots of attention in the hour before bedtime.

Eight year old Carl's severe settling problem dated from the time he was two-and-a-half years old and his sister was born. He was very demanding of attention in the evenings and would not go to sleep until his parents went up to bed. He would make a lot of noise in his room, disrupting his sister's sleep and come in and out of his room all evening, demanding food, drink, approval for his drawings, or anything that would force his parents' attention.

The aim of treatment was for Carl to learn to be independent of his parents after a given time in the evenings and to be asleep by around nine o'clock. Carl's programme combined extinction and positive reinforcement. His parents took him upstairs to bed at 8pm, spent some quiet time reading with him or talking about his drawings, and settled him after a reminder of what was expected of him. If he appeared downstairs again, his parents did not to allow themselves to be engaged in conversation or activity but took him straight back up to bed. It was agreed that for every night Carl remained upstairs, he would receive 20p towards a boglin he wanted to buy. The treatment worked rapidly: by the sixth week he was no longer coming downstairs.

Carl's mother's comments: 'The whole programme was easy enough. I suppose the pressure to be consistent was difficult at the beginning. At the end of the day I guess parents have to look at themselves and change their behaviour. That's always difficult'.

2. Providing the Conditions that Encourage Sleep

A second strategy for eliminating sleep problems is to set the scene for appropriate bedtime behaviour by introducing systematic cues and positive routines which warn the child that bedtime is approaching. This works by changing the antecedent that sets off the difficult behaviour. Many children with sleep problems do not have a regular bedtime routine, so they do not associate going to bed with going to sleep. Some children are prepared for bed hours before being put to bed or falling asleep because their parents mistakenly believe that if they start the preparation for bed early, the child might be more cooperative. Some children with visual or hearing impairments may not receive the cues that other children get that bedtime is approaching. They may not see darkness fall, for example. If your child understands that a bedtime routine is a regular part of going to bed and that he is expected to settle to sleep once in bed, he is more likely to comply. He will learn to associate going to bed with the routine. A consistent bedtime routine can make him feel secure and relaxed.

How to Start a Bedtime Routine

First, you should set a regular bedtime and stick to it. Next, you should carry out a nightly bedtime routine of four or five quiet, relaxing activities. The routine can involve anything you and your child enjoy together: preparation for bed, a drink and a biscuit, a cuddle, a story, or a song or tape of music. It should last about the same time each evening and should not be prolonged — about half an hour. Finally you should take your child to bed and settle him. Some children find a special toy or a security object is a cue for settling at night; others need a night light. Some parents we have worked with used a wind-up musical toy that played a lullaby. You should say goodnight and leave the bedroom while the child is still awake. Your child should be left to fall asleep alone. Your presence should not be used as a cue for him to fall asleep, since this produces problems if he wakes in the night to find he is alone. You should stick to this routine through thick and thin until the sleep problem disappears. You should combine this strategy with positive reinforcement, or, if the problem is very severe, with a programme of gradual distancing from the child's room.

Set a regular bedtime routine and stick to it!

Other Ways of Changing the Antecedents to Behaviour

In the same way, you can teach the child who wakes early cues to indicate when he is allowed to get up and come into your bedroom. You can put a picture of a smiling face on your bedroom door when you are ready for him to come in in the morning, or you can set an alarm in the child's room to indicate when he can get up. A child who cannot tell the time can be taught when he is allowed to get up if you stick strips of tape to the clock face at the desired getting up time, say 7.30. When the hands of the clock line up with the tapes, the child knows that he can get up. There is an ingenious alarm clock that can be bought in toyshops. It is called the 'Sleepy Time Bunny Clock'. The clock shows a rabbit, which sleeps at night, but when it is time to get up the rabbit's eyes open and ears pop up. The child can be taught that he can come into your room when the rabbit wakes up. Remember to praise your child when he responds appropriately.

Why It Works

Changing the antecedent to a behaviour seems to work by providing a new set of associations. The old antecedent — putting the child to bed without warning — triggered the difficult night-time behaviour. A new antecedent — the bedtime routine followed by taking the child to bed — will not have the same associations for the child. It will encourage him to perform the responses you desire, eg settling quietly in his bed after you have said goodnight. Each time you praise your child for settling quietly you will strengthen the association between the cue (bedtime routine) and your child's response. Katy's programme combined positive routines with graduated extinction.

Katy was a four-year-old twin with Down's Syndrome. It took at least two hours for her to settle at night. She went to bed when she was tired, often getting out of bed again many times before she finally settled. She also woke during the night and would come into her parents' bed. To make matters worse, she was in the habit of waking at around 5 am, sometimes earlier. Her treatment involved creating a bedtime routine consisting of a verbal reminder, a bath, a story, and a quiet talk downstairs. She was then taken to her own room and settled quickly by 7.30 pm. When she woke up during the night, her mother was to resettle her in her own bed with as little interaction as possible.

The programme was slow to start to work partly due to a family holiday, partly due to disagreements between Katy's parents. Her father was sceptical about the programme at first. However, when he saw that real progress was being made, his attitude changed and he began to support his wife's efforts. The programme was completed after 11 weeks. Katy stopped coming into her parents' bed completely and her settling time was reduced to a few minutes. Her mother said that she had found it difficult to become consistent and disciplined at the beginning but once she could see the benefits it became easy. 'Evenings are now a real pleasure' she said. She also reported that Katy's daytime behaviour had improved, as had that of her twin brother.

3. Extinction

What Is Extinction?

Sometimes when a child is put to bed he repeatedly comes downstairs until his parents give up and let him stay up and watch TV or play downstairs. The child has learned that his difficult behaviour produces rewards in the form of being allowed to stay up. His difficult behaviour can be extinguished by deliberately withholding the reinforcement that is maintaining it (being allowed to stay up). If his parents take him back to bed every time he comes downstairs, eventually he will stop coming downstairs and stay in his own room. This strategy for dealing with difficult behaviour is called extinction. Here are some further examples.

BEHAVIOUR	REINFORCER	EXTINCTION
Linda wakes in the night and calls out for her parents.	Cuddles and attention.	Check and ignore.
Steven has tantrums when told it's bedtime.	Postponement of bedtime.	Take to bed, settle and leave.
Jean keeps coming into her parents' bed at night.	Warmth and attention.	Take back to own bed.
Bill, aged 3, cries for a bottle during the night.	Sugary taste of the drink.	Substitute water for juice.

Extinction involves arranging conditions so that the child receives no rewards for undesirable behaviour. It means withholding reinforcements such as approval and attention that have previously been provided for the undesirable behaviour. Successful extinction results in a permanent 'unlearning' of the behaviour, which then disappears from the child's repertoire. In order to carry out extinction procedures you will need to use an ABC chart to determine all the factors that are maintaining the difficult behaviour. Often you will find that these involve social reinforcement — attention and responsiveness. If you are carrying out an extinction programme you must save your attention, responsiveness, praise, and smiles for when the child behaves correctly and ignore the child when he behaves badly.

Extinction can only be used if the difficult behaviour is being maintained by positive reinforcement. Think about your child's own sleep problems. Looking at the ABC chart you may begin to see patterns in your child's difficult bedtime behaviour. You may see that it happens at certain times in certain situations and your child may be receiving a great deal of positive reinforcement or reward. Perhaps you have got into the habit of giving way to your child's demands because it is the easiest thing to do. Sometimes you may start off being firm but give in and allow him to stay up after his difficult behaviour has gone on for a long time. If you have been rewarding the behaviour with attention and postponement of bedtime or allowing him to sleep in your bed you will have been unintentionally making it more likely that your child will repeat the behaviour. The disobedience at bedtime will continue to happen because it has a pay-off for your child. To solve the problem you will need to stop reinforcing or attending to his behaviour.

Check and ignore!

Deciding Whether to Use an Extinction Programme

Extinction progammes can be very difficult for parents to follow for a number of reasons. Firstly, all the reinforcers that maintain the problem behaviour must be identified and withheld. Sometimes it is not only your attention or approval that reinforces the child's difficult behaviour. He may derive intrinsic satisfaction and pleasure from behaving badly.

Alternatively, he may receive reinforcement from brothers and sisters. Extinctions should be used only if you can be sure that you have identified the motivation for your child's behaviour.

Secondly, you must expect that in the early stages the problem will get worse rather than better. When you start to ignore his bad behaviour the child may cry or scream for a very long time in order to get his way or he may shout that he is ill, thirsty or hurt. It is essential that you persist with the programme and do not reinforce these behaviours by giving in and comforting your child. This can be very hard to do. Extinction programmes most commonly fail because parents lose their resolve before the child loses his undesirable behaviour. If you want to use an extinction programme, do not underestimate the difficulty of ignoring problem behaviour. The following questions may help you to decide whether an extinction programme is right for you and your child.

1. Is it possible to identify all the reinforcers maintaining the problem behaviour?
2. Can you decide how you will withhold them?
3. Will you be able to continue if the behaviour worsens temporarily?
4. Will the activities the child may engage in be dangerous if you ignore them?

Rules for Using Extinction

There are three basic rules for carrying out extinction procedures:

1. Where possible you should state clearly and firmly what is required of your child before leaving the bedroom.
2. You have to carry out the agreed course of action every time the problem occurs. If you do not do this, you will find the behaviour harder than ever to eliminate.
3. You must realise that if you want to use this method then you must be persistent. You must continue to withhold reinforcement by leaving the child until the crying has stopped before you go in or by being prepared to take him back to bed and leave him there, even if he cries for a long time or throws a temper tantrum.

Extinction programmes can be very hard to carry out. While an extinction programme is in progress, neighbours may have to be told what is happening if the increase in noise is likely to disturb them. Similarly, you may have to change brothers' and sisters' sleeping places so they will not be disturbed. It is important for parents of children with physical or mental disabilities to check with their GP before starting an extinction programme.

This will alleviate fears that the child may become sick if left to cry. In addition, both parents must be fully committed to the programme. If one parent is less committed than the other the programme can be undermined. Despite the problems, extinction programmes can bring very swift results if you are brave enough to try them and feel that you can cope with the temporary worsening of the problem when you start. If you have any doubts, try a more gradual programme of change instead.

Mary's programme combined extinction, positive routines, and positive reinforcement.

Mary was a nine year old and had severe settling problems, refusing to stay in her bed when she was settled for the night. Every night she either played about upstairs, shouting and throwing her toys around, disturbing her younger sister, or she repeatedly came downstairs to her parents. She also woke two or three times during the night, disturbing her parents by calling for attention. Mary's mother said that she felt totally exhausted by the end of every evening.

Treatment involved deciding on a suitable bedtime for Mary and following a set routine every night. Mary was given a drink and biscuit and put to bed after a story and a cuddle. She was then put back to bed immediately every time she came downstairs or got up, with a minimum amount of interaction. The same course of action was followed when she awoke during the night. Mary was rewarded with praise if she stayed in her bed. The treatment worked very rapidly, and Mary stopped waking at night completely. She also stopped getting out of bed except on a very few occasions when a request from her mother was sufficient to get her back into bed. Settling time decreased from over an hour to about twenty minutes and Mary started to fall asleep about half an hour earlier. Mary's mother was delighted with the result and reported that Mary's daytime behaviour had also improved. She reported feeling less stressed, and better supported.

Mary's mother's comments: 'I am very satisfied. It was a good exercise to keep the diary, which showed us precisely what was happening before you started working with us. Things definitely did change for the better.'

4. Gradual Stages of Change (Graduated Extinction)

What Is Graduated Extinction?

An alternative method for eliminating sleep problems is to bring about a more gradual change in the child's behaviour. Programmes based on these strategies are generally more popular with parents and work very well. They avoid the problem of leaving the child to cry it out. They are useful if your child refuses to go to bed unless you lie down with him or if he insists on being rocked to sleep in your arms. Instead of leaving the child to cry, you gradually distance yourself from his room in a series of steps.

How to Carry Out a Graduated Extinction Programme

First you sit by the bed holding your child's hand and stroking him. Then when he settles without fuss, you gradually move your chair step by step from the room on subsequent evenings until you are sitting first by the bedroom door, then outside it with the door open. During the course of the programme you should have as little interaction as possible with your child. You are there to see that he is not coming to any harm. You are not there to reinforce his behaviour by games, smiles, and cuddles after you have settled him in his bed. Each of the steps should be firmly established before you move on to the next step. Eventually when your child settles quickly on his own, you no longer need to sit outside the bedroom door and can go and enjoy your evening.

A variation of this strategy can be used if your child wakes in the night or cries after being put to bed. You can wait a few minutes longer each night before you go to check on him. This is usually called the controlled crying technique. Eventually your child will learn that his crying is not being rewarded and will stop making a fuss. If your child keeps getting out of bed, you can use a similar method to teach him to stay in bed at night. You will need to close the door of his bedroom for an increasing number of minutes each time he gets out of bed. For a child who will not go to bed when you want him to, you can gradually bring bedtime forward in a series of steps, by 10 minutes each night.

Here is the case history of a child with whom we used a graduated extinction programme.

Jenny was a three-and-a-half year old child who would not settle to sleep on her own. She insisted that her mother lay down on the bed with her, cuddling her closely as she fell asleep. She also woke two or three times a night and again her mother had to lie down with her until she returned to sleep. A graded approach to both settling and waking problems was used. Jenny's mother began by lying down with Jenny but not cuddling her. Jenny was given a teddy bear to cuddle instead. Jenny's mother gradually reduced contact with her daughter by lying down each night for a shorter time and moving to sit on a chair near the bed. By week 3 she was spending less time lying down with Jenny and more time sitting on the chair. When Jenny awoke during the night her mother sat by her bed until she fell asleep again. After a few weeks Jenny started coming into her parents' room when she woke. Jenny's mother took her straight back to bed, settled her and left the room.

By week 8 Jenny was able to settle to sleep alone in her own bed and her wakings were fewer. By week 11 she was scarcely waking at all. Jenny's mother was delighted with the results and has since had another child.

Jenny's mother's comments: 'The way the programme was done in steps was excellent. We're really delighted. It was really interesting to write down what was happening and then to see how much improvement had been made'.

Points to Remember

A child's behaviour is determined by its antecedents and consequences. If the consequences are rewarding, the child will be more likely to repeat the behaviour. In order to change behaviour we can change either the antecedent or the consequence. We can make the consequences of night-time behaviour rewarding by reinforcing the child whenever she shows appropriate night-time behaviour. We can alter the consequences of difficult behaviour by not attending to the child when she cries or by otherwise removing the incentive for it. We can change the antecedent, which is usually the child being put to bed, by teaching the child cues that bedtime is approaching. Finally, we can introduce a more gradual programme of change.

- **Positive reinforcement** is the systematic rewarding of appropriate night-time behaviour.
- **Providing the conditions that encourage sleep** means setting the scene for the desired bedtime behaviour by providing systematic cues and positive routines.
- **Extinction** is the systematic withholding of a reinforcer that is maintaining undesirable night-time behaviour.
- **Graduated extinction** involves a programme of gradual change such as gradual distancing of the parent from the child's room.

TEST YOUR KNOWLEDGE OF BEHAVIOURAL METHODS

The following questionnaire tests your knowledge of behavioural methods applied to sleep. Simply read the questions and tick the letter that you think represents the correct answer for each one.

1. Most night-time difficulties in young children are probably:
   (a) a reaction to deeper emotional problems.
   (b) due to lack of communication in the home.
   (c) accidentally taught by the child's parents.
   (d) due to a stage that the child will outgrow.

2. Jane, aged six, begins to whine and cry when her mother puts her to bed and leaves the bedroom at night. How should her mother react?
   (a) Ask Jane why she wants her mother to stay with her.
   (b) Explain to Jane that it is the parents who decide when it is bedtime.
   (c) Stay for a while and talk to Jane.
   (d) Ignore the whining and crying.

3. Probably the most important idea to keep in mind when trying to improve bedtime behaviour is:
   (a) to use both reward and punishment.
   (b) to reward every time the child goes to bed without fuss.
   (c) to be flexible in whether or not you reward.
   (d) to make sure the child understands why you want her behaviour to change.

4. Desirable and undesirable bedtime behaviour are most alike in that they are:
   (a) the result of emotions and feelings.
   (b) habits and therefore difficult to change.
   (c) ways the child expresses himself.
   (d) the result of learning.

5. Which of the following is the most important for parents in controlling their child's bedtime behaviour?
   (a) The rules parents make about bedtime behaviour.
   (b) The parents' understanding of the child's feelings at bedtime.
   (c) The bedtime behaviours to which the parents attend.
   (d) Being strict but also warm and gentle.

6. If you are trying to teach a child appropriate bedtime behaviour you should first:
   (a) reward the child at weekends when he has settled for a week without fuss.
   (b) reward the child in the morning when he has settled for a night without fuss.
   (c) reward the child when he settles immediately in his bed.
   (d) punish the child for not settling.

7. Parents who use lots of rewards for good bedtime behaviour will probably tend to have children who:
   (a) do not understand discipline.
   (b) will not cooperate unless they are 'paid'.
   (c) take advantage of their parents.
   (d) are cooperative and do not make a fuss about going to bed.

8. Terry wakes often during the night and calls out for his mother. The best way to teach Terry not to disturb his mother is to:
   (a) go to him and tell him off severely when it occurs.
   (b) praise and hug him in the morning when he has not disturbed her.
   (c) explain carefully to him how important it is that she gets a good night's sleep.
   (d) tell him she won't take him to the zoo if it continues.

9. David has been rewarded each time he has settled quietly to sleep. In order to get him to settle without using a reward, the next step should probably be:
   (a) to have a talk about how pleased you are and then stop giving the reward.
   (b) to give the reward about one in five times.
   (c) to give the reward almost every time.
   (d) to continue giving the reward each time.

10. Sally often wakes up and cries at night. In trying to find out why, her mother should probably consider the possibility that:
    (a) Sally is trying to tell her something.
    (b) Sally needs more of her attention.
    (c) she is somehow rewarding Sally's crying.
    (d) Sally is not tired.

11. A good behavioural rule is:
    (a) do not reward with money if possible.
    (b) catch a child doing something right.
    (c) reward good behaviour and always punish bad behaviour.
    (d) punishment is always unnecessary.

12. To record and note the direction of bedtime behaviour change is:
    (a) a minor optional step in a behaviour change programme.
    (b) an important step in a behaviour change programme.
    (c) a procedure only employed by scientists for research.
    (d) time-consuming and complicated, so only for use in special cases.

13. Punishment, as a way to extinguish undesirable bedtime behaviour, is best used when:
    (a) you are very upset.
    (b) you want to teach the child the right way to behave.
    (c) the behaviour may be dangerous.
    (d) telling off doesn't seem to be effective.

14. Sheila keeps coming into her parents' bed during the night. Her parents decide to praise her when she stays in her own bed. However, she still keeps coming. What is probably happening?
    (a) Sheila doesn't want her parents' praise.
    (b) The benefits of coming into her parents' bed are stronger than her parents' praise.
    (c) She is at a stage she will grow out of.
    (d) She gets lonely at night.

15. Joe will not go to bed at night. His mother has decided to change this and wants to measure the relevant behaviours. Which is the best way for her to do this?
    (a) Each evening record what time Joe goes to bed.
    (b) Chart his behaviour all day long to find out what causes his not wanting to go to bed.
    (c) Each week make a note of how easy or difficult it has been to get him to bed.
    (d) Ask Joe to keep his own record each week.

16. The first step in changing difficult bedtime behaviour is to:
    (a) reward the child when she goes to bed on time.
    (b) punish the child for misbehaviour when she refuses to go to bed.
    (c) observe the behaviour carefully.
    (d) ask someone who is more objective for advice.

17. In changing bedtime settling behaviour it is most important to use:
    (a) methods that have been tested by others.
    (b) consequences that are rewarding to the child.
    (c) consequences that are punitive towards the child.
    (d) rewards that do not bribe the child.

18. Peter is exhibiting severe settling and waking problems. He also wakes up very early in the morning and disturbs his parents. It would be best to:
    (a) try quickly to eliminate all these undesirable behaviours at once.
    (b) select just two behaviours to deal with at first.
    (c) select the single behaviour that is causing most problems and concentrate on changing that.
    (d) wait for a month before beginning to try to change his behaviours to make sure they are stable and persistent.

19. Jill cries and makes a fuss when told it is bedtime. What would be a good way to teach her to go to bed on time?
    (a) Start putting her to bed half an hour earlier than usual.
    (b) Let Jill stay up until she is tired.
    (c) Start a regular bedtime routine about half an hour before Jill's normal bedtime.
    (d) Play a noisy game before bedtime to tire Jill out.

20. Alice, aged eight and severely epileptic, wakes up and cries for her parents several times a night. What should her parents do?
    (a) Go to her immediately and comfort her whenever she cries.
    (b) Punish her for disturbing her parents.
    (c) Check on her and quietly leave the room if she is alright.
    (d) Ignore her crying.

21. Stuart keeps coming into his parents' bedroom at night and getting into their bed. How can his mother change this behaviour?
    (a) Punish Stuart whenever he comes into their room.
    (b) Take Stuart back to bed immediately every time he gets into his parents' bed.
    (c) Change beds with Stuart so he sleeps with his dad.
    (d) Let him stay for a while and then take him back to his own bed.

22. Which of the following is probably the most important in teaching a child desirable behaviour?
    (a) Teaching him the importance of self-discipline.
    (b) Helping him to understand right and wrong.
    (c) Providing him with consistent consequences for his bedtime behaviour.
    (d) Understanding why he misbehaves.

23. How often a child wakes and calls out for his parents is mostly controlled by:
    (a) the child's temperament.
    (b) what happens to him at the same time as he wakes and cries.
    (c) what happens to him just before he wakes and cries.
    (d) what happens to him just after he wakes and cries.

24. Listed below are four methods used to change behaviour. Which is usually the best technique to get a child to go to bed at night?
    (a) Punish him when he won't go to bed.
    (b) Ignore him when he won't go to bed.
    (c) Reward him when he goes to bed promptly.
    (d) Explain to him why his behaviour is undesirable.

Answers

1 c 7 d 13 c 19 c
2 d 8 b 14 b 20 c
3 b 9 c 15 a 21 b
4 d 10 c 16 c 22 c
5 c 11 b 17 b 23 d
6 c 12 b 18 c 24 c

How well did you do?
0-6 Not very good. You need to look at this chapter again.
7-12 Quite good, but it would be worth re-reading the chapter when you have time.
13-18 Very good. You have a good understanding of the behavioural principles.
19-24 Excellent. You have understood the behavioural principles very well indeed.

When you are happy that you have understood the behavioural methods you will be ready to begin dealing with your child's sleep problem. The charts in Part III will help you to identify the problem and will guide you to an appropriate treatment programme.

PART III

IDENTIFYING YOUR CHILD'S SLEEP PROBLEM

How To Use The Charts

By now you will probably have a good idea of the nature of your child's sleep problem and how it is being maintained. The charts in this section will help you to check your diagnosis. Each chart takes a common symptom as its starting point and leads you by a series of simple Yes or No questions to a logical conclusion about the nature of your child's sleep problem. You will then be directed to a section of Part IV containing a detailed description of the sleep problem and, where appropriate, a programme for solving it. Before starting a treatment, read the advice at the beginning of Part IV on how to carry out a programme. Occasionally you will be advised to seek further help from your doctor or to ask to be referred to a hospital that has laboratory facilities for assessing specific sleep problems.

To find the chart you need, look up your child's main problem behaviour in the chartfinder index on the next page. This should be the behaviour that you have written in the 'B' section of the ABC chart. If you cannot find the main behaviour in the chartfinder, look for a chart dealing with a secondary sleep behaviour if your child has one. Then turn to the page number indicated and proceed with the identification of the problem.

CHARTFINDER

Babies 0-12 Months

Page

Chart 1 Baby is difficult to settle at bedtime, cries and fusses 83

Chart 2 Baby wakes during the night and cries 85

Chart 3 Baby wakes early in the morning (before 5am) 88

Chart 4 Baby suffers from excessive sleepiness during the day 89

Chart 5 Baby suffers from restless sleep or moves about strangely during sleep 90

Children 1-12 Years

Chart 6 Child is difficult to settle at bedtime, refuses to go to bed, or keeps coming downstairs 91

Chart 7 Child wakes during the night and cries or calls out for parents 93

Chart 8 Child wakes early in the morning (before 5 am) 96

Chart 9 Child suffers from excessive sleepiness or drowsiness during the day 97

Chart 10 Child suffers from restless sleep or moves about strangely during sleep ... 99

Chart 11 Child has frightening dreams or wakes up in the night confused and disoriented 100

Chart 12 Child sleeps at inappropriate times (late bedtimes and very early waking) 101

Chart 13 Child's sleep is disrupted by events that occur during sleep, sometimes causing waking or partial waking 102

Teenagers 13-18 Years

Chart 14 Teenager insists on going to bed late and sleeping late 105

Chart 15 Teenager complains of excessive daytime sleepiness or drowsiness throughout the day or sleeps during the day 106

Chart 16 Teenager complains of difficulty in falling asleep or staying asleep 108

Chart 17 Teenager's sleep is disrupted by events that occur during sleep, sometimes causing waking or partial waking 111

Chart 1 Babies 0-12 Months

Baby is difficult to settle at bedtime, cries and fusses

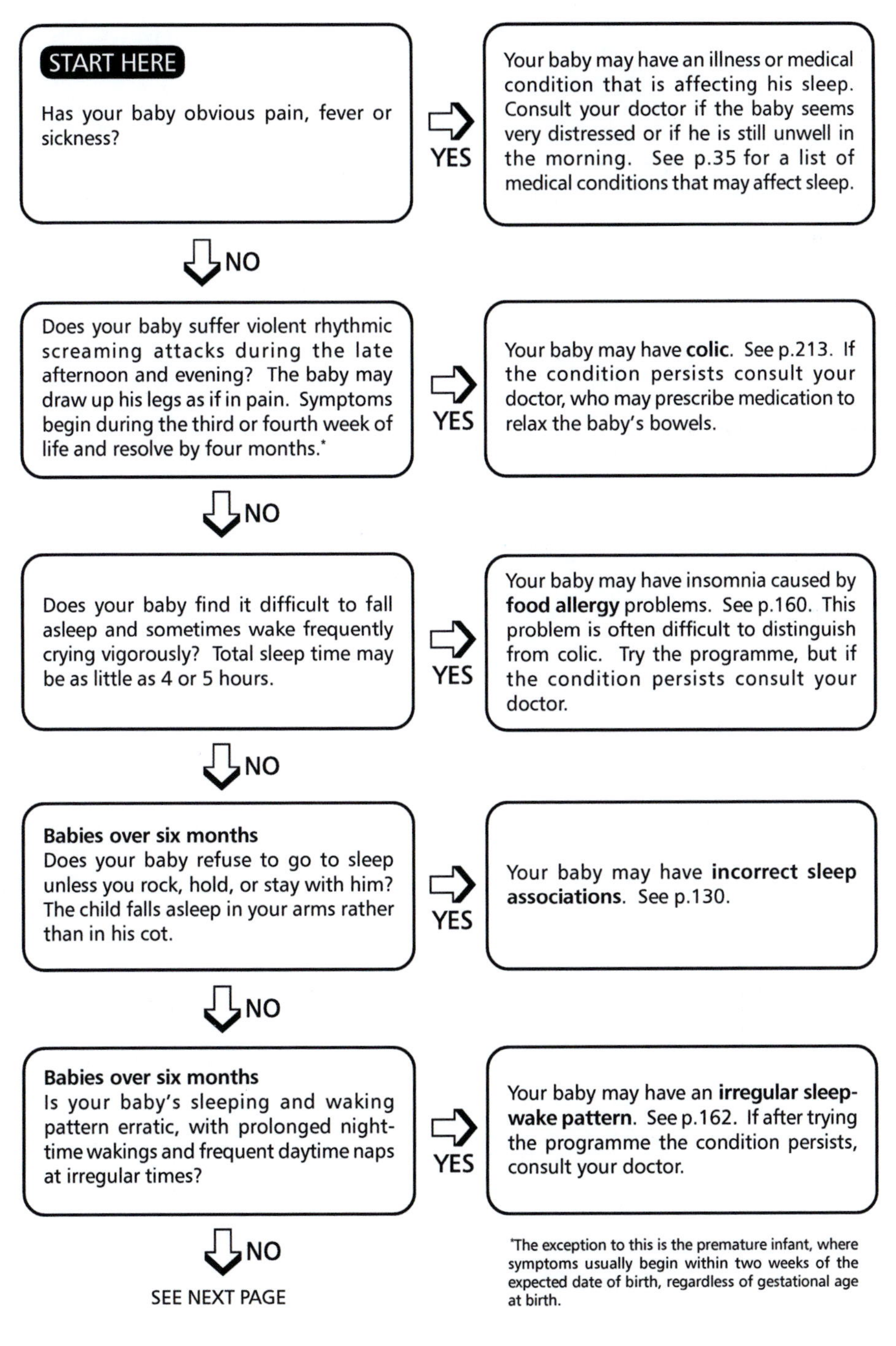

*The exception to this is the premature infant, where symptoms usually begin within two weeks of the expected date of birth, regardless of gestational age at birth.

SEE PREVIOUS PAGE

Babies over six months
Has your baby's sleep period shifted so that he goes to sleep much later than you wish, sleeps normally, but is difficult to wake in the morning and sleepy during the day?

YES

Your baby may have developed a **late sleep phase**. See p.166

Babies over six months
If you have been unable to diagnose your baby's problem from this chart, try Programme 1. If your baby does not respond, consult your doctor.

CHART 2 BABIES 0-12 MONTHS

Baby wakes during the night and cries

If your baby is under six months old and he wakes and cries in the night, he is probably hungry. By about six months of age your baby's sleep pattern will have consolidated and he will sleep for most of the night with only brief wakings. There are some problems that may disrupt the sleep of the baby of less than six months and they are noted here. Apart from dealing with these problems you should not start a sleep programme for a baby of less than six months. However, it is never too early to encourage good sleep habits even in the very young child. Read the principles of sleep hygiene on page 26. If your baby has not settled by five or six months you can consult the lower part of this chart.

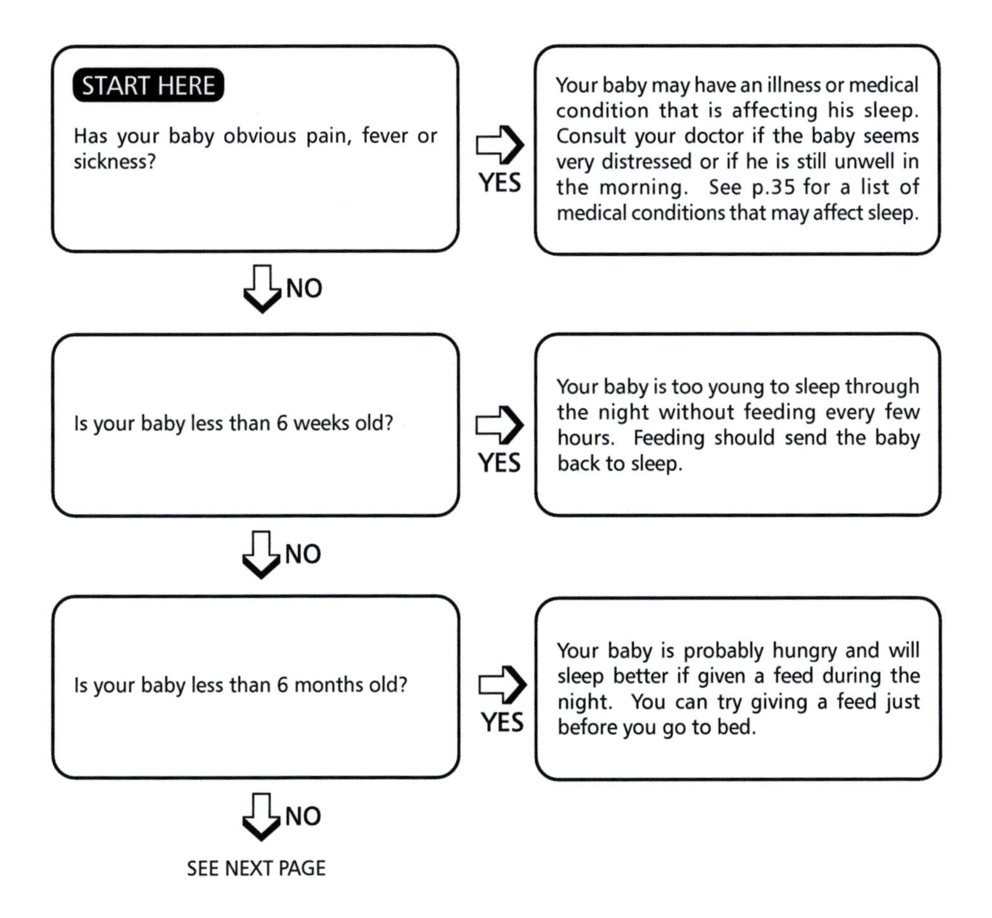

SEE PREVIOUS PAGE

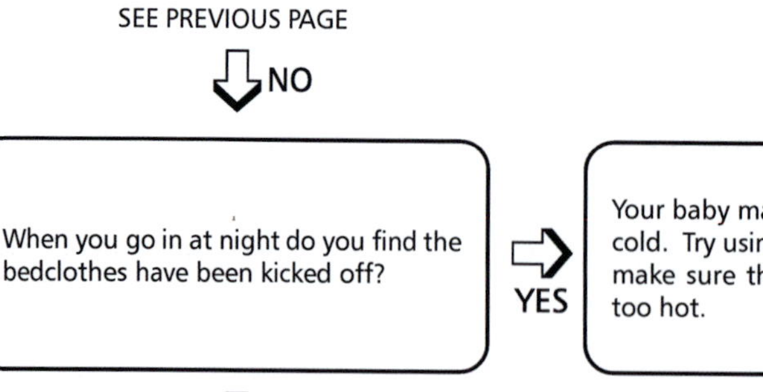

NO

When you go in at night do you find the bedclothes have been kicked off?

YES → Your baby may be waking because he is cold. Try using a baby sleeping suit, but make sure that the baby does not get too hot.

NO

Does your baby's bottom look red and sore?

YES → Your baby may be waking because he has nappy rash, which stings when he wets his nappy.

NO

Does your baby suffer violent rhythmic screaming attacks during the late afternoon and evening? The baby may draw up his legs as if in pain. Symptoms begin during the third or fourth week of life and resolve by four months.*

YES → Your baby may have **colic**. See p.213. If the condition persists consult your doctor, who may prescribe medication to relax the baby's bowels.

NO

Does your baby sometimes wake frequently crying vigorously? Total sleep time may be as little as 4 or 5 hours.

YES → Your baby may have a **food allergy** that affects his sleep. See p.160. This problem is often difficult to differentiate from colic. If the condition persists consult your doctor.

NO

Babies over six months
Does your baby wake and refuse to go back to sleep unless you rock or cuddle him? The child falls asleep in your arms rather than in his cot.

YES → Your baby may have **incorrect sleep associations**. See p.130.

NO

SEE NEXT PAGE

*The exception to this is the premature infant, where symptoms usually begin within two weeks of the expected date of birth.

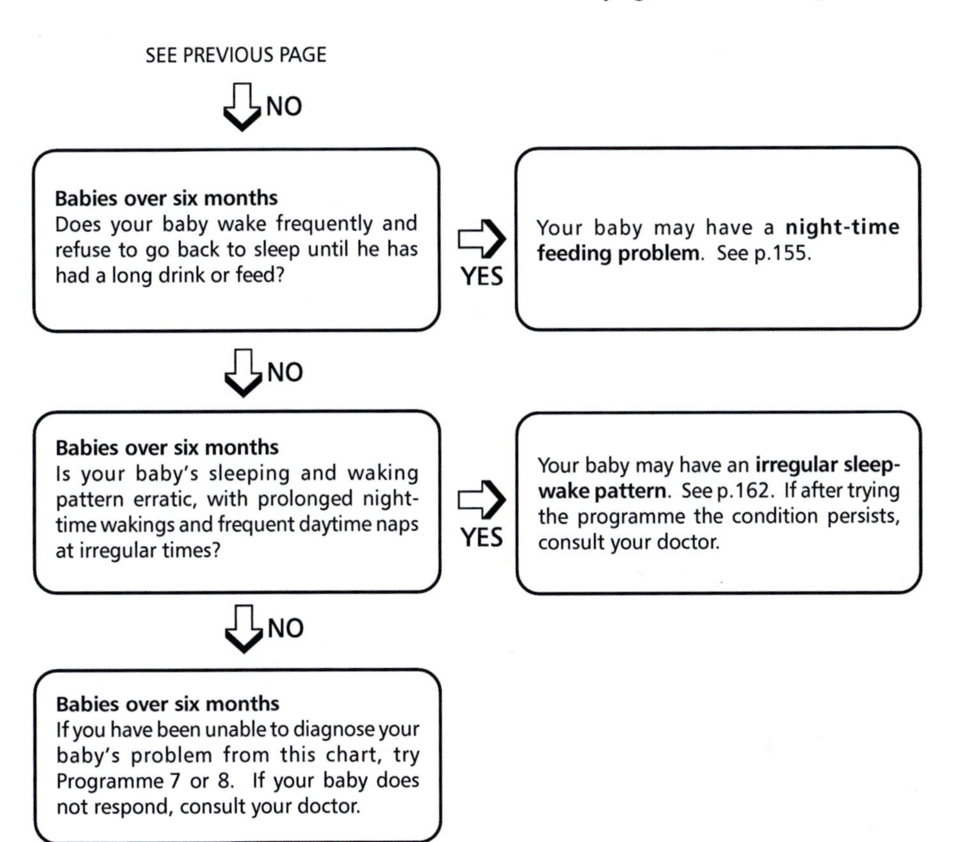
SEE PREVIOUS PAGE
NO
Babies over six months
Does your baby wake frequently and refuse to go back to sleep until he has had a long drink or feed?
YES
Your baby may have a night-time feeding problem. See p.155.
NO
Babies over six months
Is your baby's sleeping and waking pattern erratic, with prolonged night-time wakings and frequent daytime naps at irregular times?
YES
Your baby may have an irregular sleep-wake pattern. See p.162. If after trying the programme the condition persists, consult your doctor.
NO
Babies over six months
If you have been unable to diagnose your baby's problem from this chart, try Programme 7 or 8. If your baby does not respond, consult your doctor.

CHART 3 BABIES 6-12 MONTHS

Baby wakes early in the morning (before 5 am)

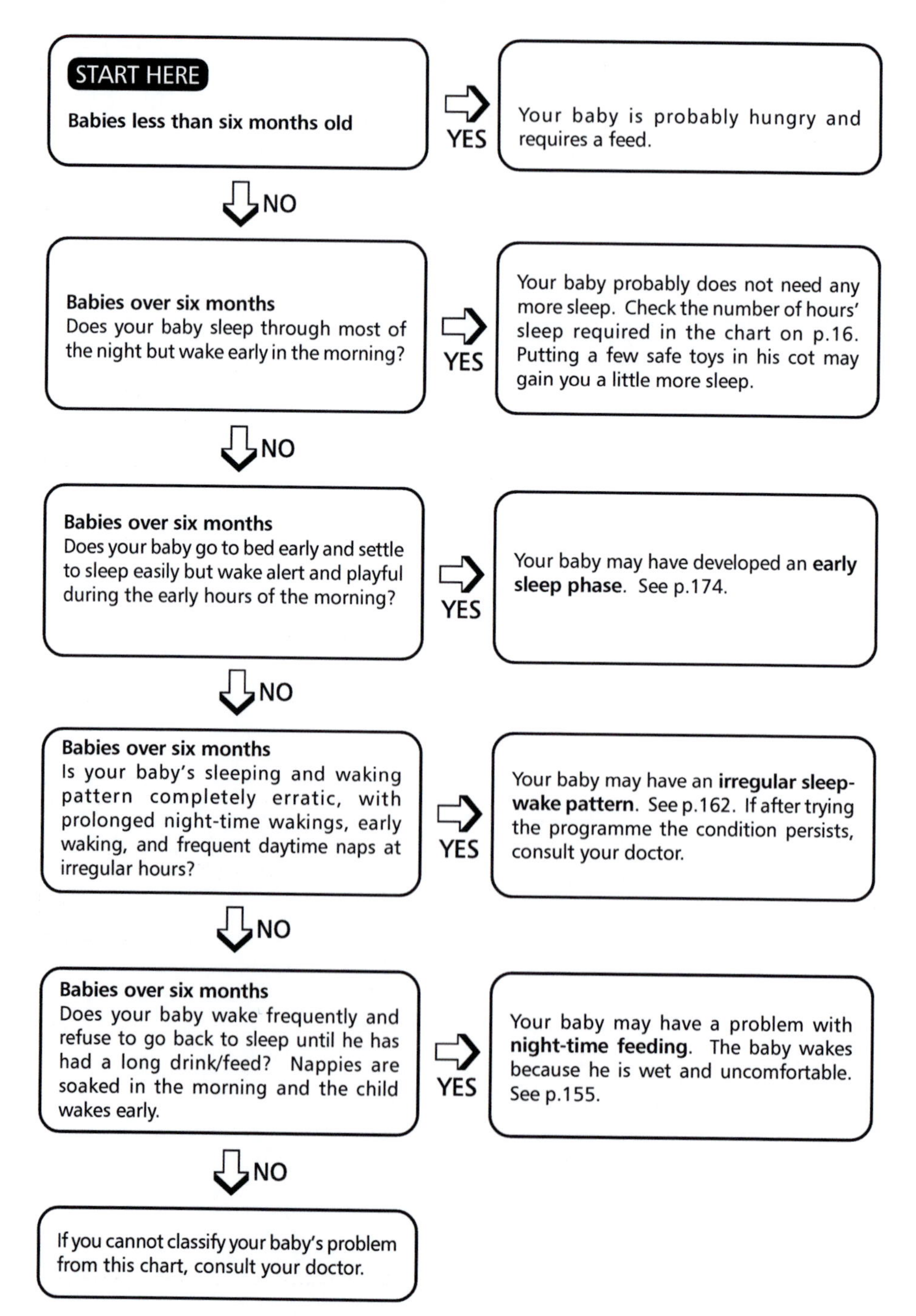

Chart 4 Babies 6-12 Months

Baby suffers from excessive sleepiness during the day*

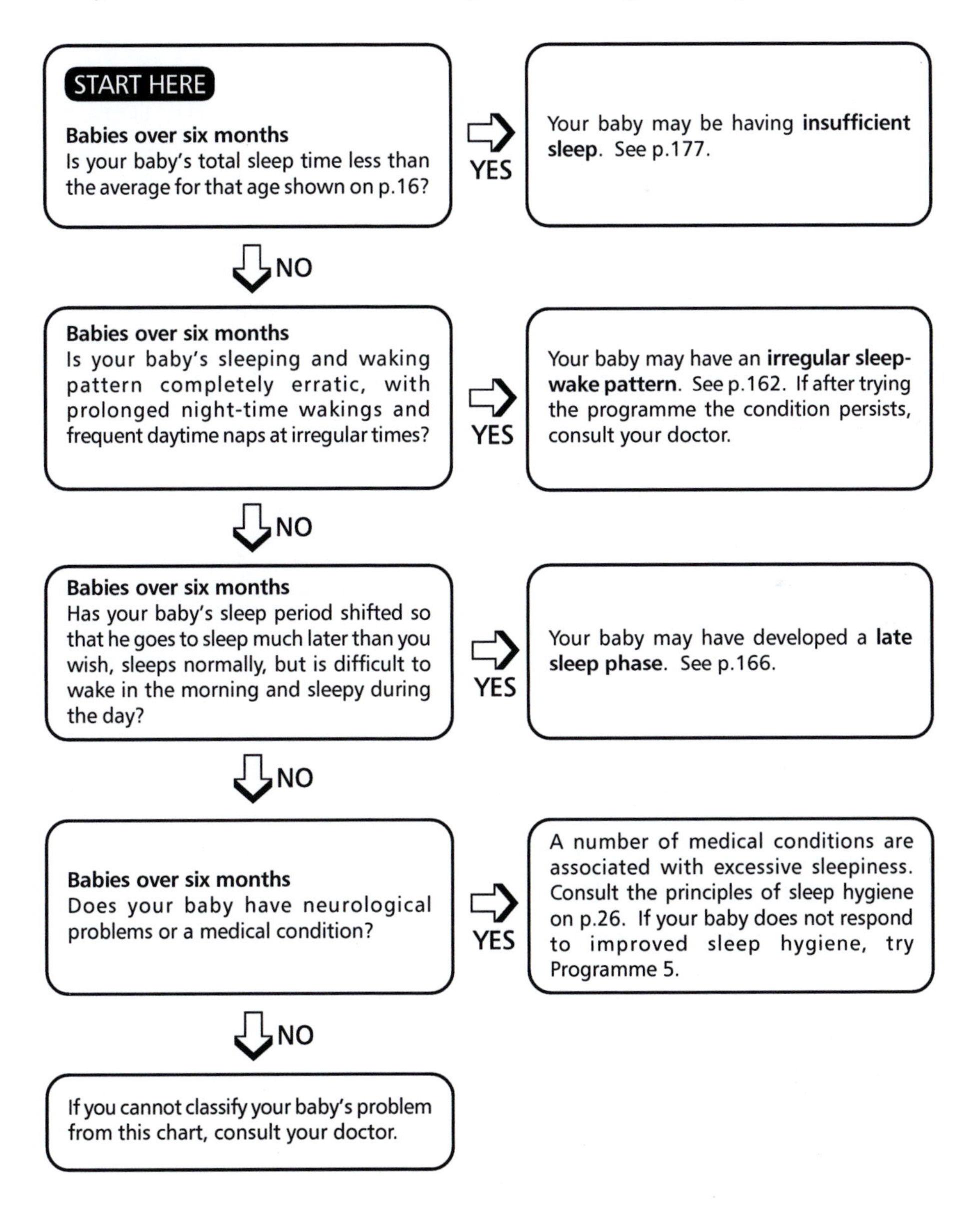

*Check the chart on p. 16 to see how much daytime sleep your baby should be taking.

Chart 5 Babies 0-12 Months

Baby suffers from restless sleep or moves about strangely during sleep

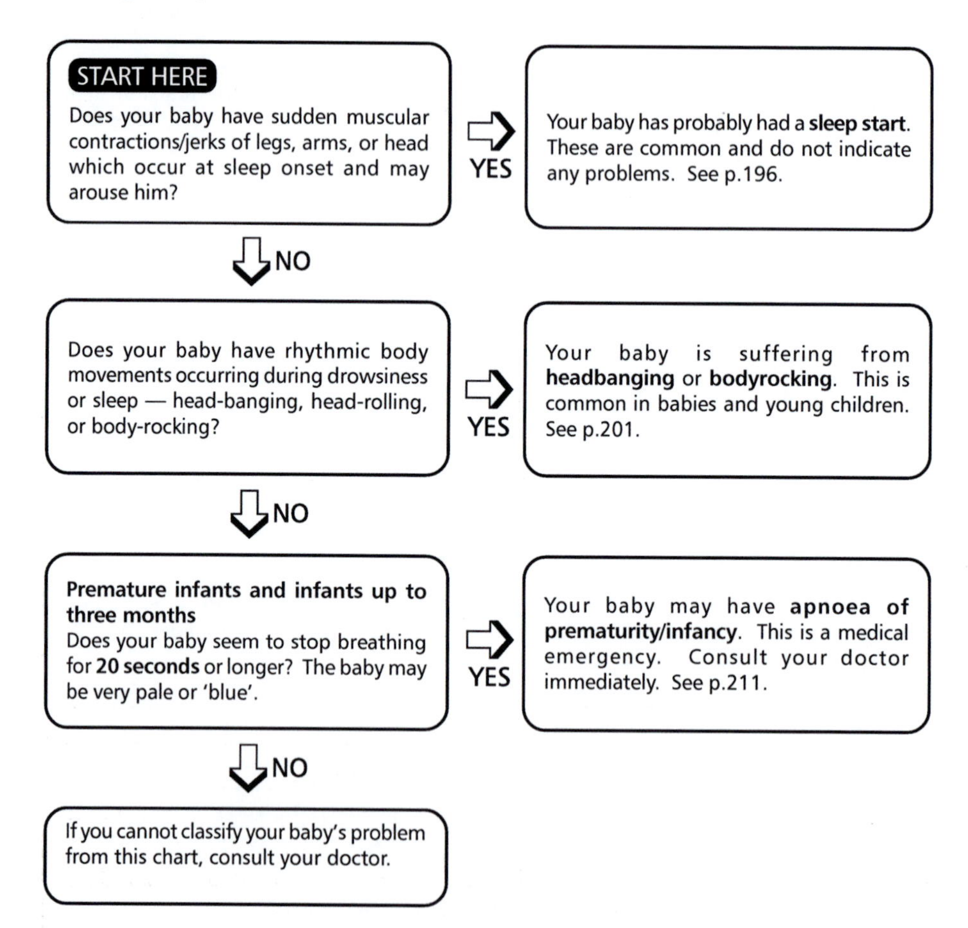

CHART 6 CHILDREN 1-12 YEARS

Child is difficult to settle at bedtime, refuses to go to bed or keeps coming downstairs

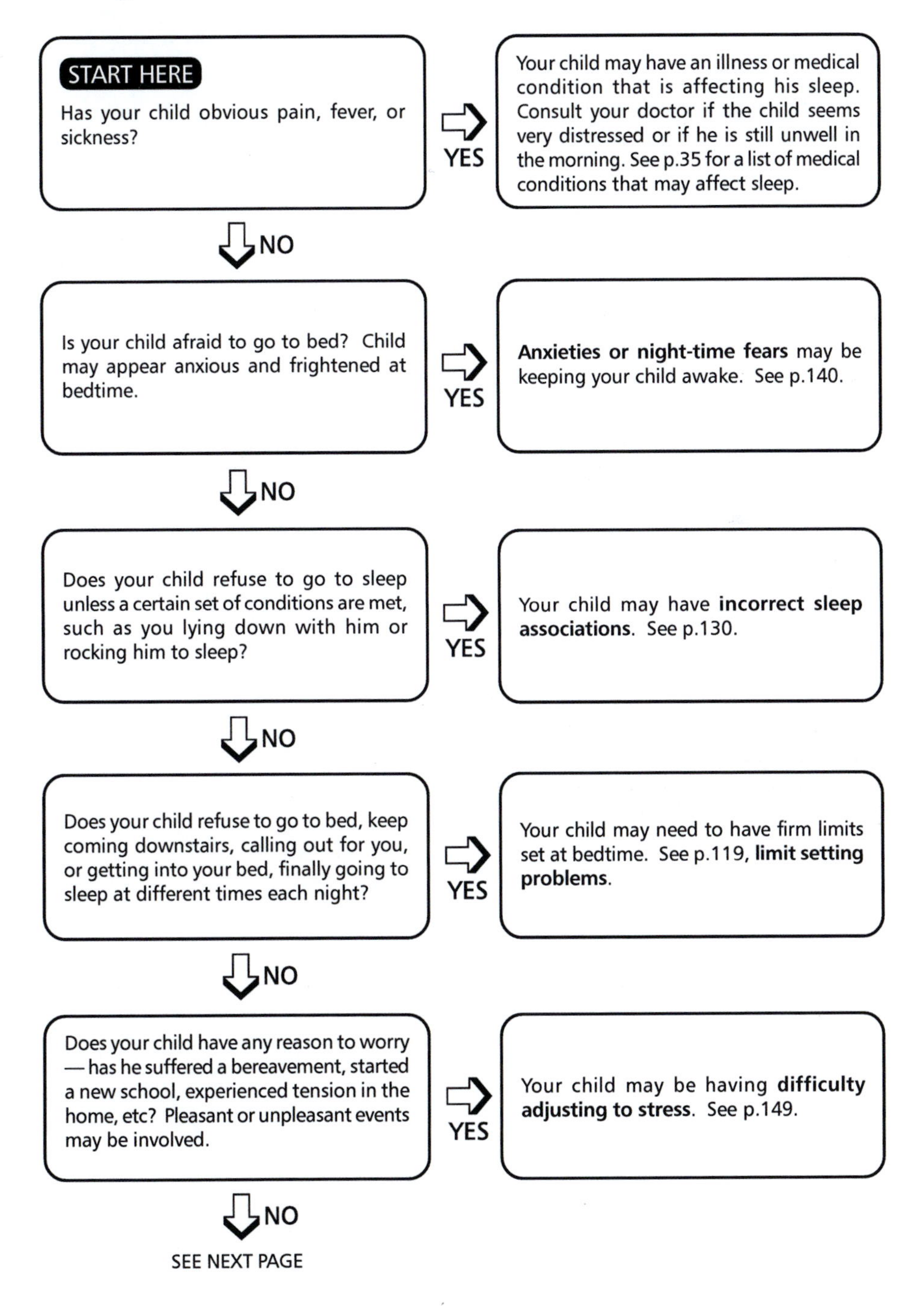

SEE PREVIOUS PAGE

NO

Does your child find it hard to fall asleep and sometimes wake frequently, crying vigorously? Total sleep time may be as little as 4 or 5 hours.

YES

Your child may have insomnia caused by **food allergy** problems. See p.160. If the condition persists consult your doctor.

NO

Has your child's sleep period shifted so that he goes to sleep much later than you wish, sleeps normally, but is difficult to wake in the morning and sleepy during the day?

YES

Your child may have developed a **late sleep phase**. See p.166. But consider **limit setting problems** first, p.119.

NO

Is your child's sleeping and waking pattern completely erratic, with bedtime battles, prolonged night-time wakings, early waking, frequent daytime naps at irregular times, or sleepiness during the day?

YES

Your child may have an **irregular sleep-wake pattern**. See p.162. If after trying the programme the condition persists, consult your doctor.

NO

If you have been unable to diagnose your child's problem from this chart, try Programme 1 or 3. If your child does not respond, consult your doctor.

Chart 7 Children 1-12 Years

Child wakes during the night and cries or calls out for parents

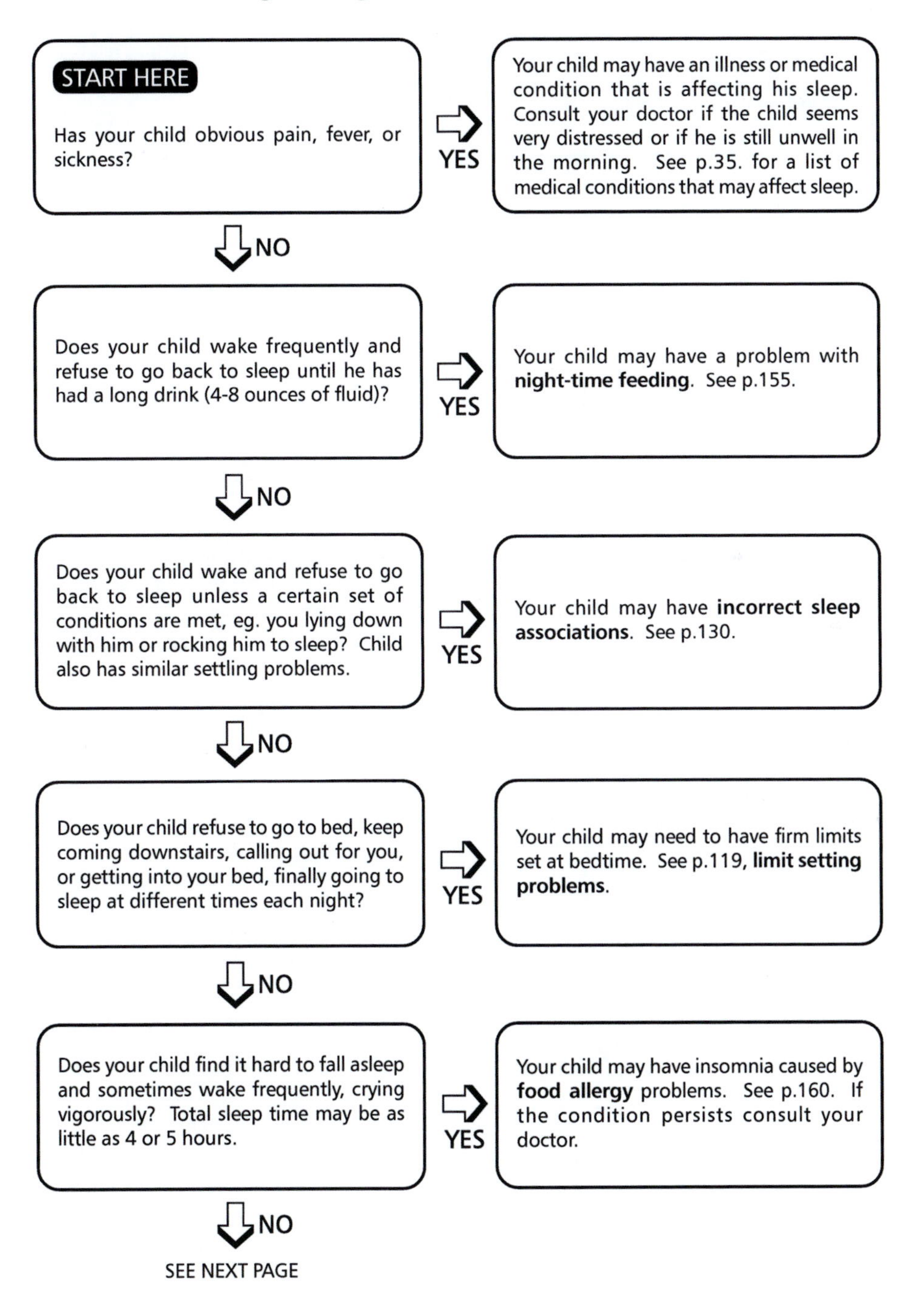

SEE PREVIOUS PAGE

NO

Does your child want to go to bed early, settling easily, but wake unduly early in the morning (before 5 am) and have frequent naps during the day?

YES → Your child may have developed an **early sleep phase**. See p.174.

NO

Is your child's sleeping and waking pattern completely erratic, with bedtime battles, prolonged night-time wakings, early waking, frequent daytime naps at irregular times, or sleepiness during the day?

YES → Your child may have **an irregular sleep-wake pattern**. See p.162. If after trying the programme the condition persists, consult your doctor.

NO

Does your child wake up in the night with fears? Child may appear anxious and frightened at bedtime.

YES → **Anxieties or night-time fears** may be waking your child. See p.140.

NO

Does your child wake up in the first third of the sleep period confused and disoriented but is not frightened and goes back to sleep? He may thrash about in bed or mumble incoherently. He will not remember the event the next day. Children under five are more vulnerable to this problem.

YES → Your child may have had a **confusional arousal**. See p.187.

NO

Does your child wake in the night feeling frightened and anxious, complaining of nightmares or frightening dreams? These happen in the last third of the sleep period. The child will remember the dream and find it difficult to return to sleep until comforted.

YES → Your child has probably had a **nightmare**. See p.198, and p.194, **differences between sleep terrors and nightmares.**

NO

SEE NEXT PAGE

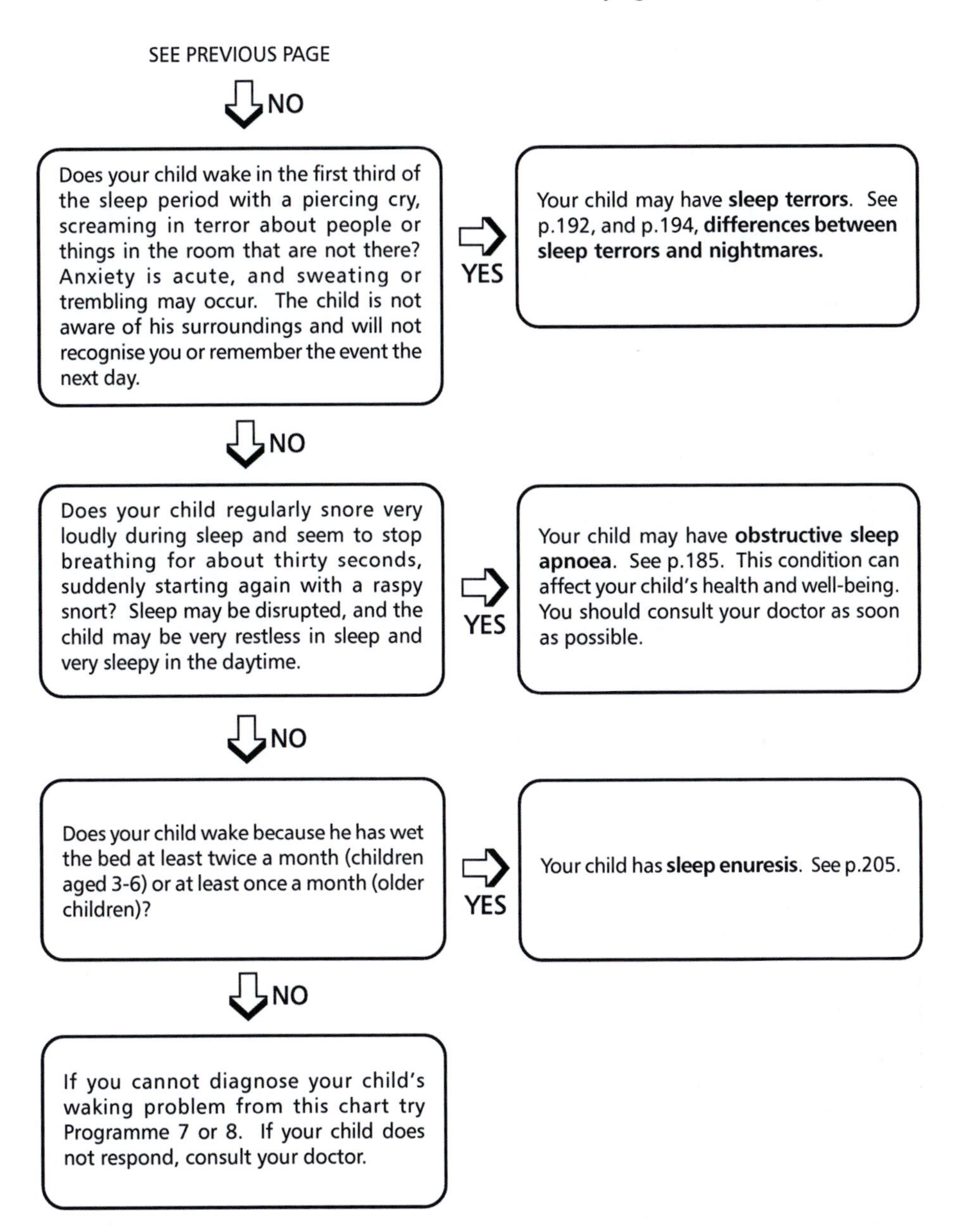
SEE PREVIOUS PAGE
NO
Does your child wake in the first third of the sleep period with a piercing cry, screaming in terror about people or things in the room that are not there? Anxiety is acute, and sweating or trembling may occur. The child is not aware of his surroundings and will not recognise you or remember the event the next day.
YES
Your child may have **sleep terrors**. See p.192, and p.194, **differences between sleep terrors and nightmares.**
NO
Does your child regularly snore very loudly during sleep and seem to stop breathing for about thirty seconds, suddenly starting again with a raspy snort? Sleep may be disrupted, and the child may be very restless in sleep and very sleepy in the daytime.
YES
Your child may have **obstructive sleep apnoea**. See p.185. This condition can affect your child's health and well-being. You should consult your doctor as soon as possible.
NO
Does your child wake because he has wet the bed at least twice a month (children aged 3-6) or at least once a month (older children)?
YES
Your child has **sleep enuresis**. See p.205.
NO
If you cannot diagnose your child's waking problem from this chart try Programme 7 or 8. If your child does not respond, consult your doctor.

CHART 8 CHILDREN 1-12 YEARS

Child wakes early in the morning (before 5am)

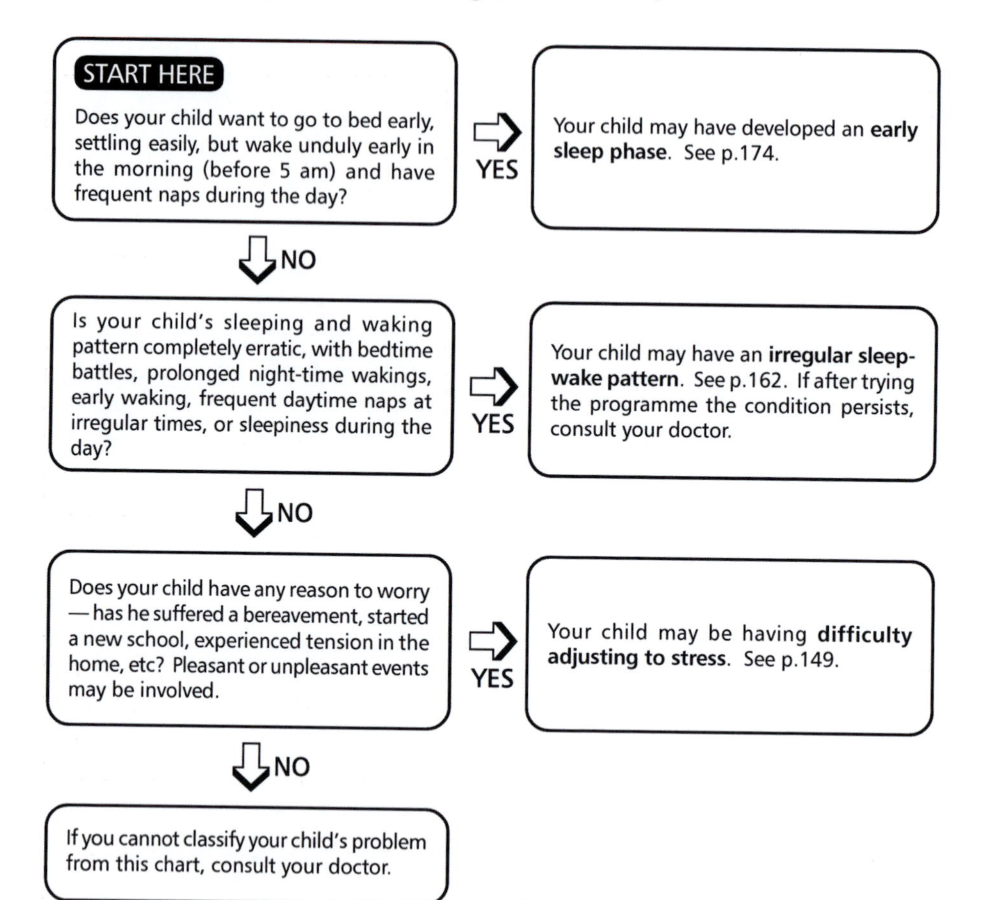

Chart 9 Children 1-12 Years

Child suffers from excessive sleepiness or drowsiness during the day

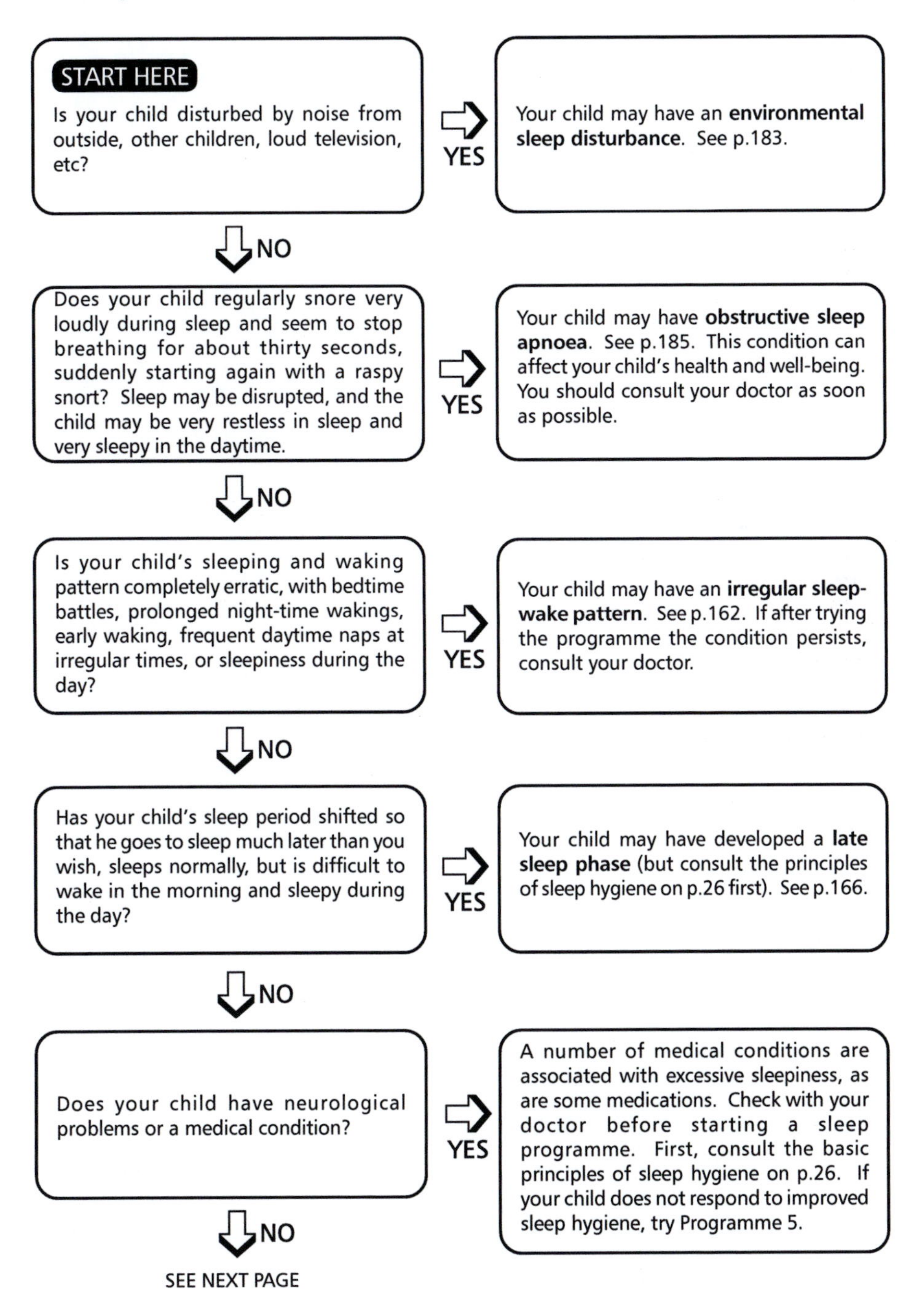

SEE PREVIOUS PAGE

NO

Is your child's total sleep time less than the average for that age shown on p.16?

YES

Your child may be having **insufficient sleep**. Check the amount of sleep your child needs on p.16. See p.177.

If you cannot classify your child's problem from this chart, consult your doctor.

Chart 10 Children 1-12 Years

Child suffers from restless sleep or moves about strangely during sleep

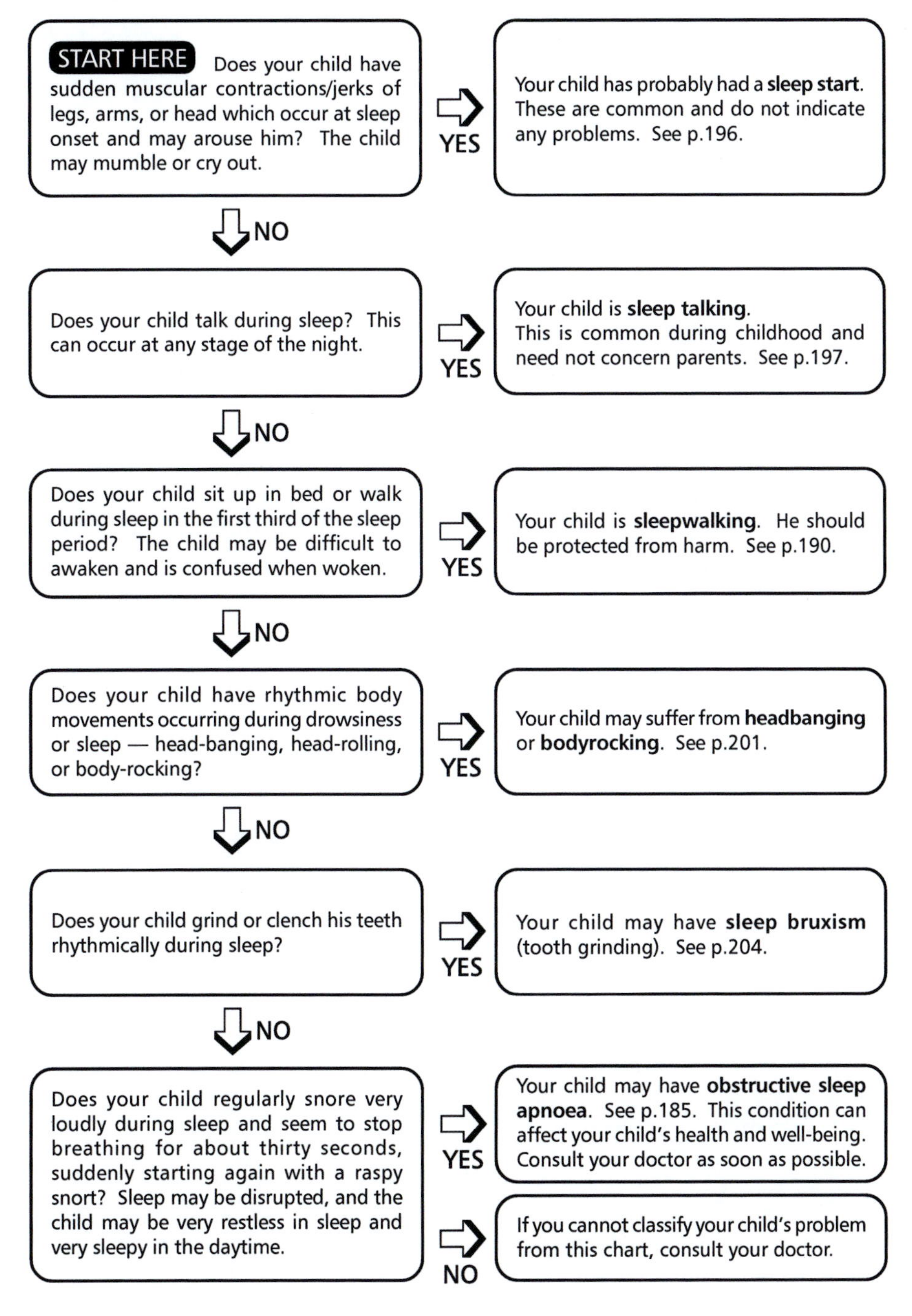

Chart 11 Children 1-12 Years

Child has frightening dreams or wakes up in the night confused and disoriented

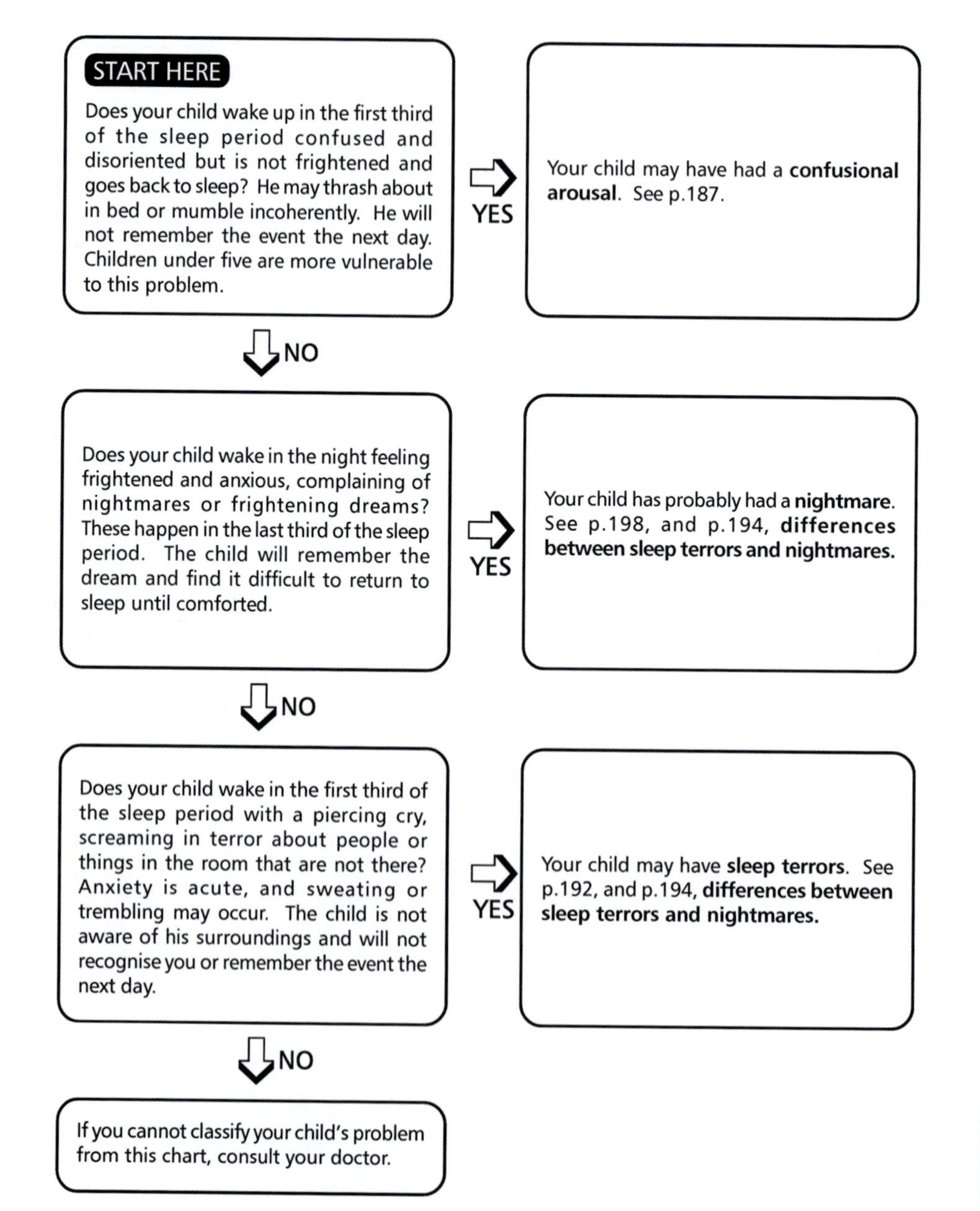

Chart 12 Children 1-12 Years

Child sleeps at inappropriate times (late bedtimes and very early waking)

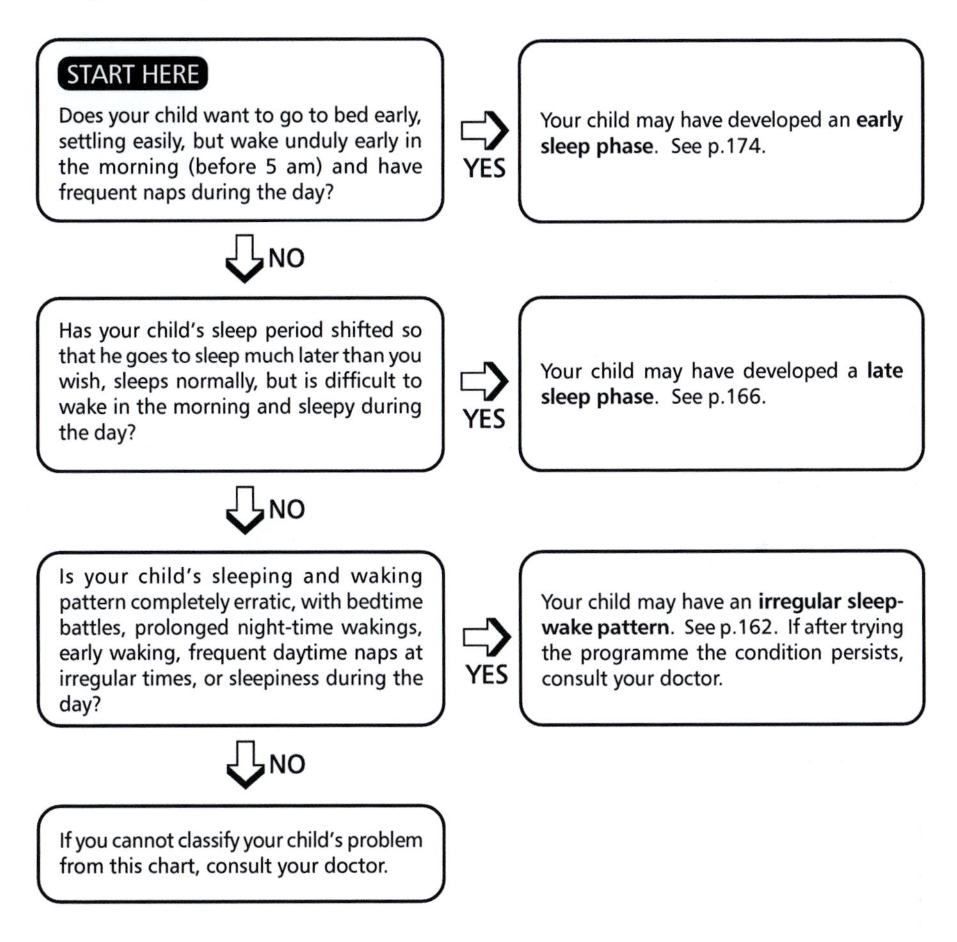

Chart 13 Children 1-12 Years

Child's sleep is disrupted by events that occur during sleep, sometimes causing waking or partial waking

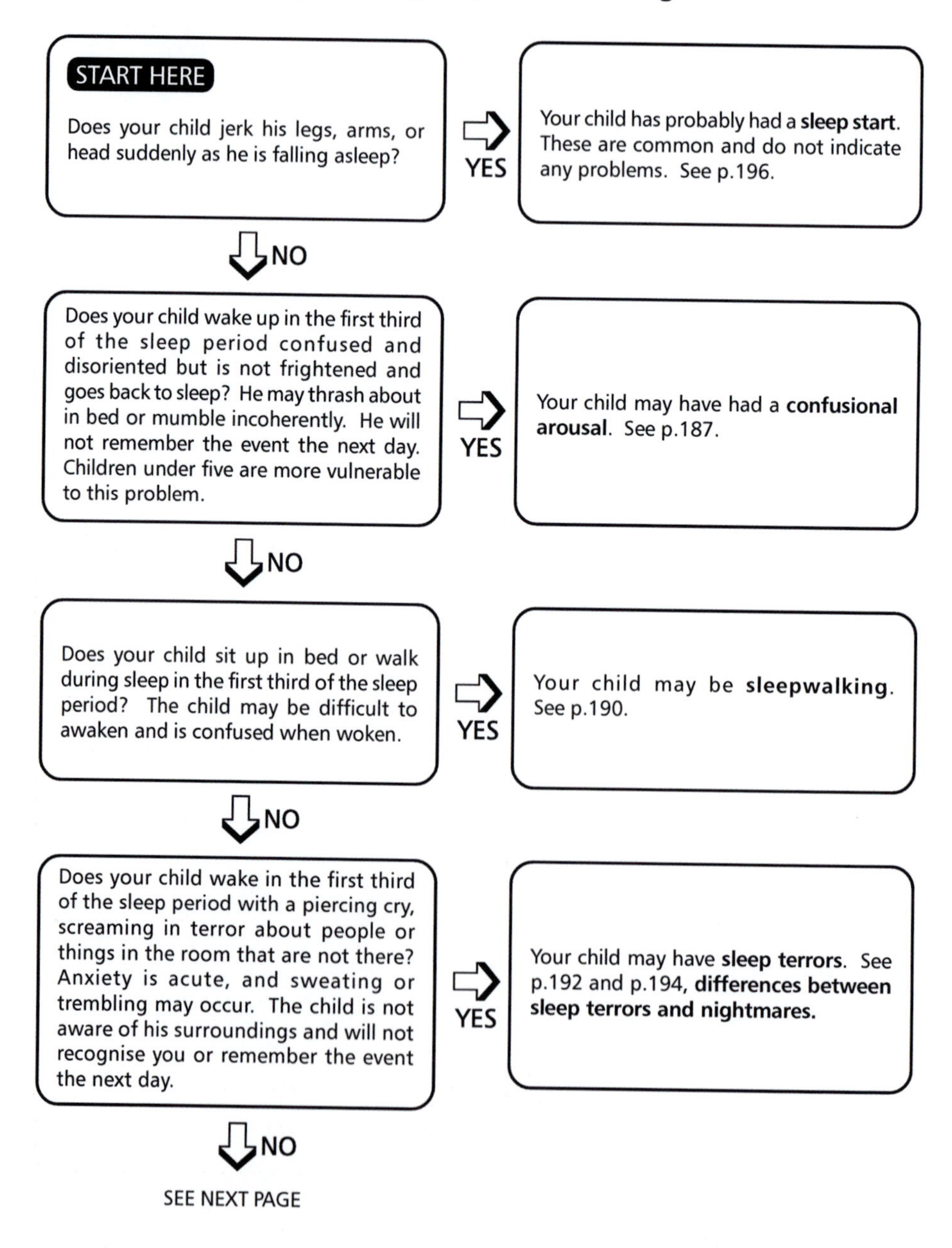

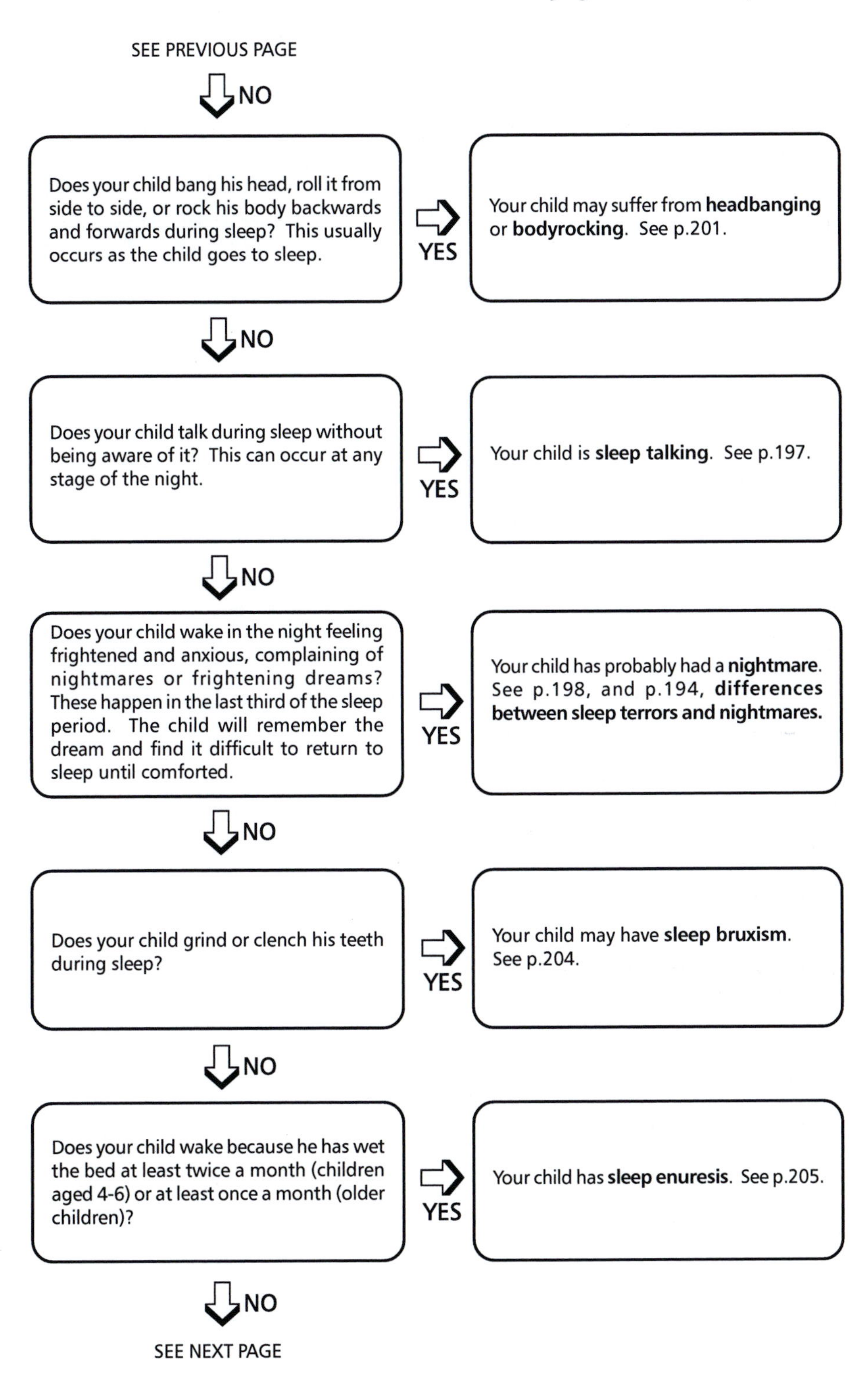
SEE PREVIOUS PAGE
NO
Does your child bang his head, roll it from side to side, or rock his body backwards and forwards during sleep? This usually occurs as the child goes to sleep.
YES
Your child may suffer from **headbanging** or **bodyrocking**. See p.201.
NO
Does your child talk during sleep without being aware of it? This can occur at any stage of the night.
YES
Your child is **sleep talking**. See p.197.
NO
Does your child wake in the night feeling frightened and anxious, complaining of nightmares or frightening dreams? These happen in the last third of the sleep period. The child will remember the dream and find it difficult to return to sleep until comforted.
YES
Your child has probably had a **nightmare**. See p.198, and p.194, **differences between sleep terrors and nightmares.**
NO
Does your child grind or clench his teeth during sleep?
YES
Your child may have **sleep bruxism**. See p.204.
NO
Does your child wake because he has wet the bed at least twice a month (children aged 4-6) or at least once a month (older children)?
YES
Your child has **sleep enuresis**. See p.205.
NO
SEE NEXT PAGE

SEE PREVIOUS PAGE

Does your child regularly snore very loudly during sleep and seem to stop breathing for about thirty seconds, suddenly starting again with a raspy snort? Sleep may be disrupted, and the child may be very restless in sleep and very sleepy in the daytime.

YES →

Your child may have **obstructive sleep apnoea**. See p.185. This condition can affect your child's health and well-being. You should consult your doctor as soon as possible.

If you cannot classify your child's problem from this chart, consult your doctor.

The following disorders occur when teenagers have reached the stage where they can choose their own bedtime.

Chart 14 Teenagers 13-18 Years

Teenager insists on going to bed late and sleeping late

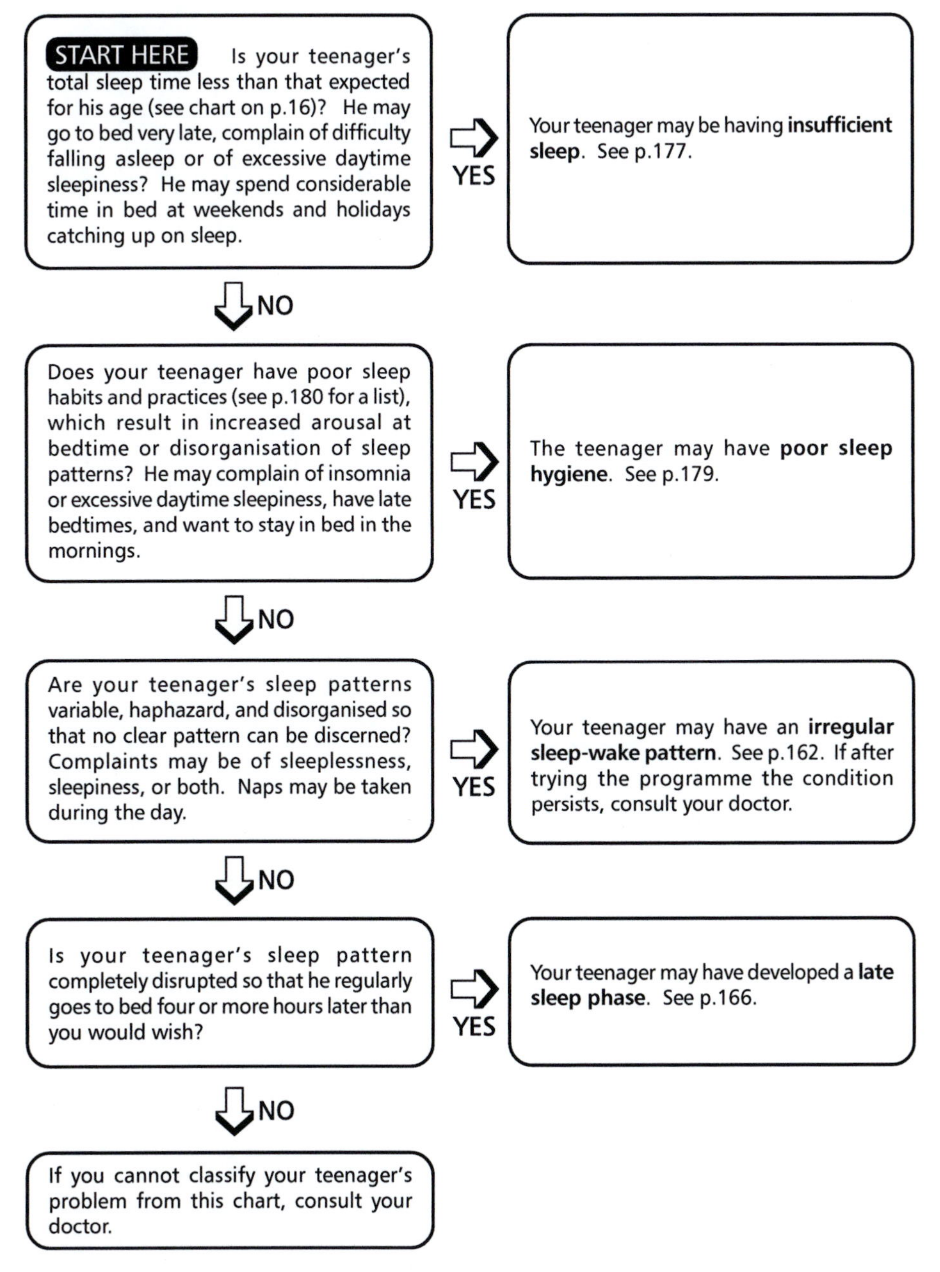

CHART 15 TEENAGERS 13-18 YEARS

Teenager complains of excessive daytime sleeepiness or drowsiness throughout the day or sleeps during the day

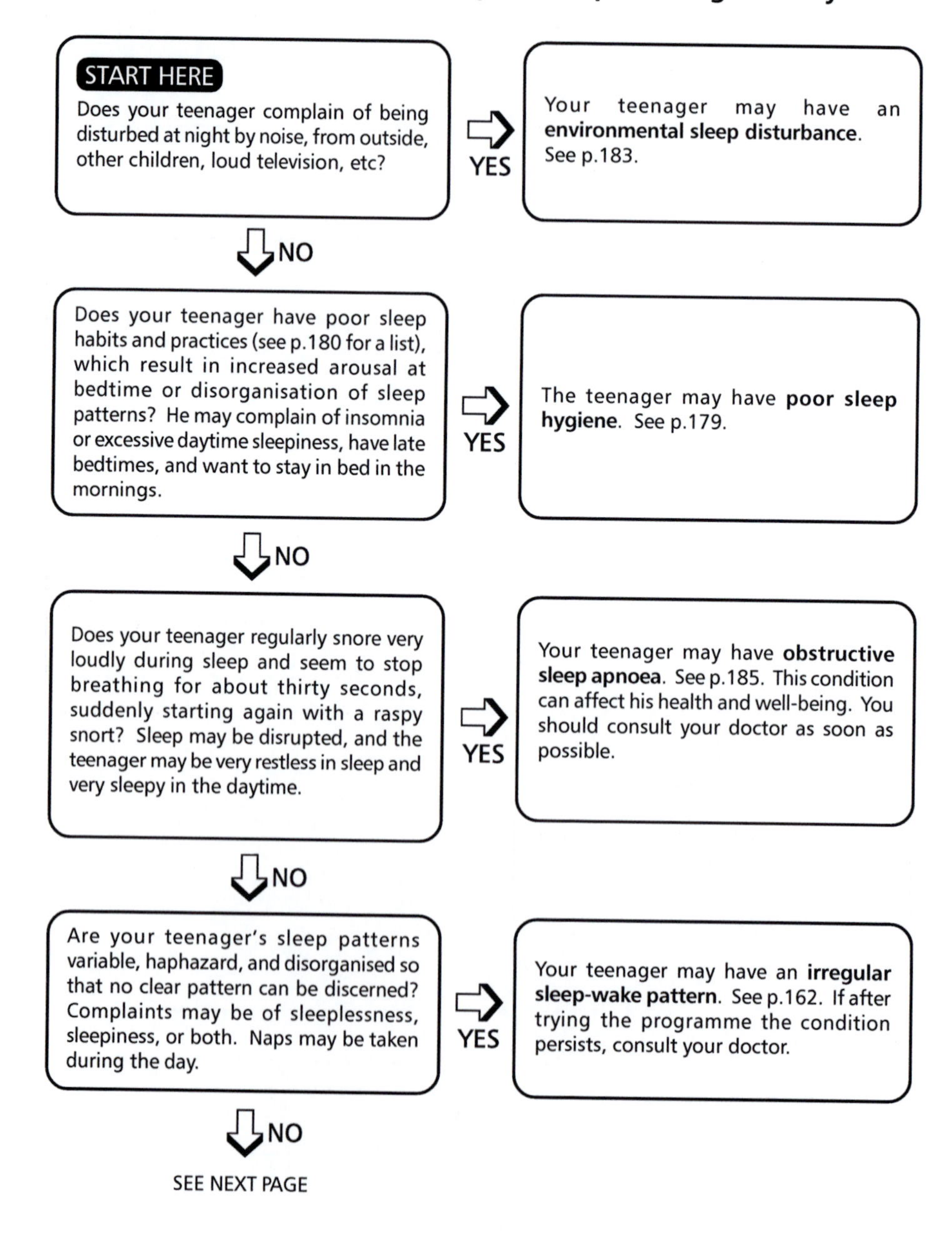

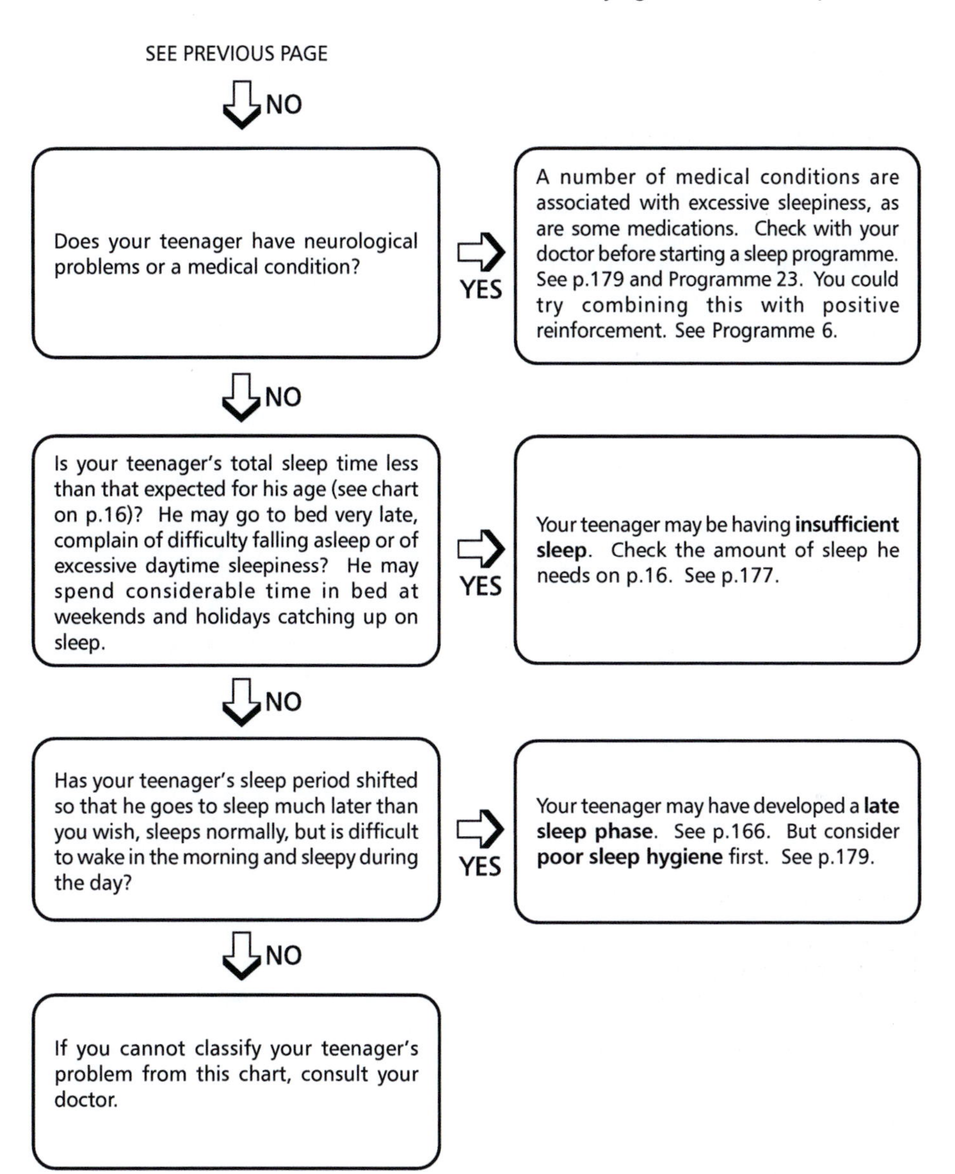
SEE PREVIOUS PAGE
NO
Does your teenager have neurological problems or a medical condition?
YES
A number of medical conditions are associated with excessive sleepiness, as are some medications. Check with your doctor before starting a sleep programme. See p.179 and Programme 23. You could try combining this with positive reinforcement. See Programme 6.
NO
Is your teenager's total sleep time less than that expected for his age (see chart on p.16)? He may go to bed very late, complain of difficulty falling asleep or of excessive daytime sleepiness? He may spend considerable time in bed at weekends and holidays catching up on sleep.
YES
Your teenager may be having **insufficient sleep**. Check the amount of sleep he needs on p.16. See p.177.
NO
Has your teenager's sleep period shifted so that he goes to sleep much later than you wish, sleeps normally, but is difficult to wake in the morning and sleepy during the day?
YES
Your teenager may have developed a **late sleep phase**. See p.166. But consider **poor sleep hygiene** first. See p.179.
NO
If you cannot classify your teenager's problem from this chart, consult your doctor.

Chart 16 Teenagers 13-18 Years

Teenager complains of difficulty in falling asleep or staying asleep

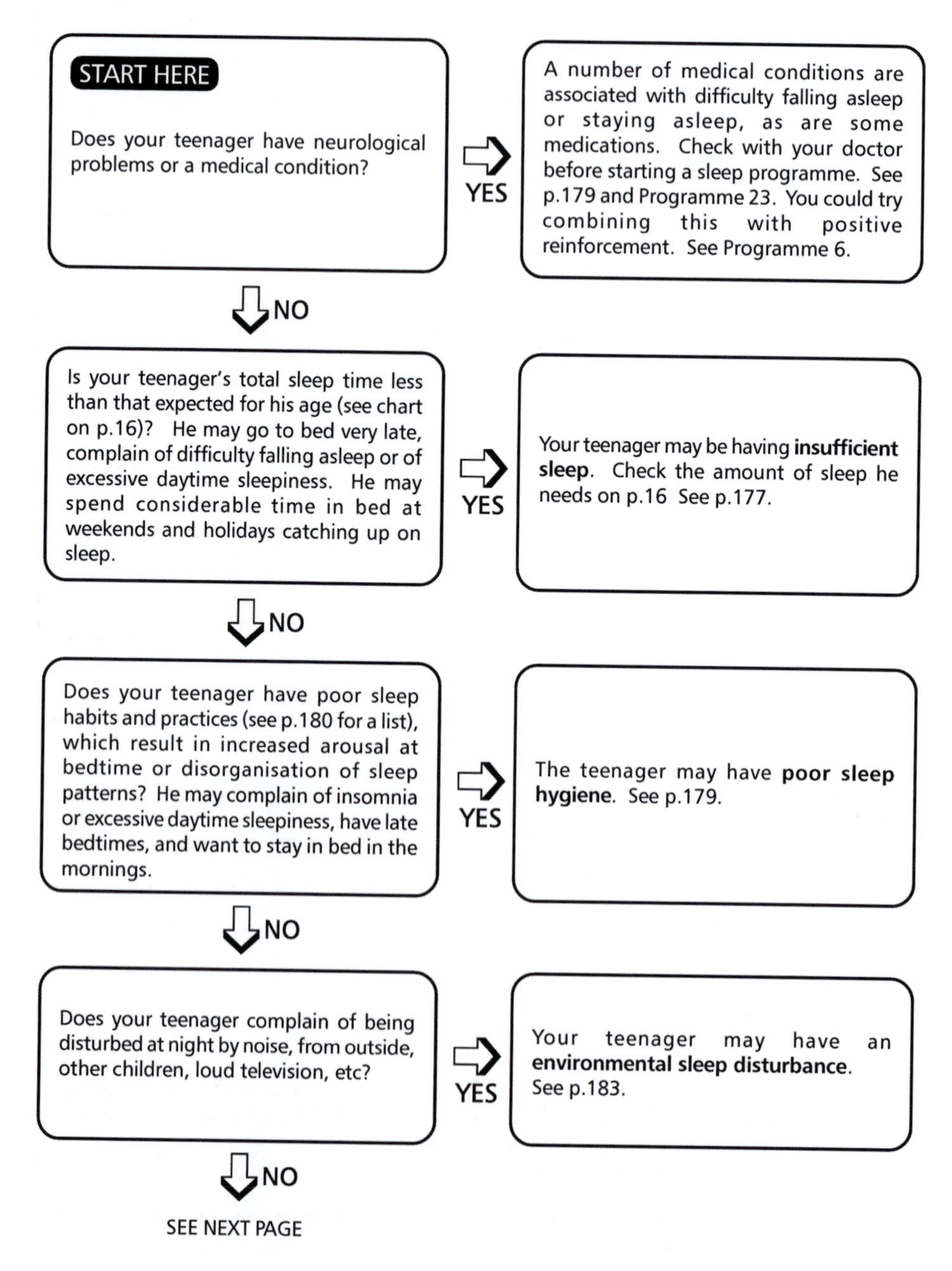

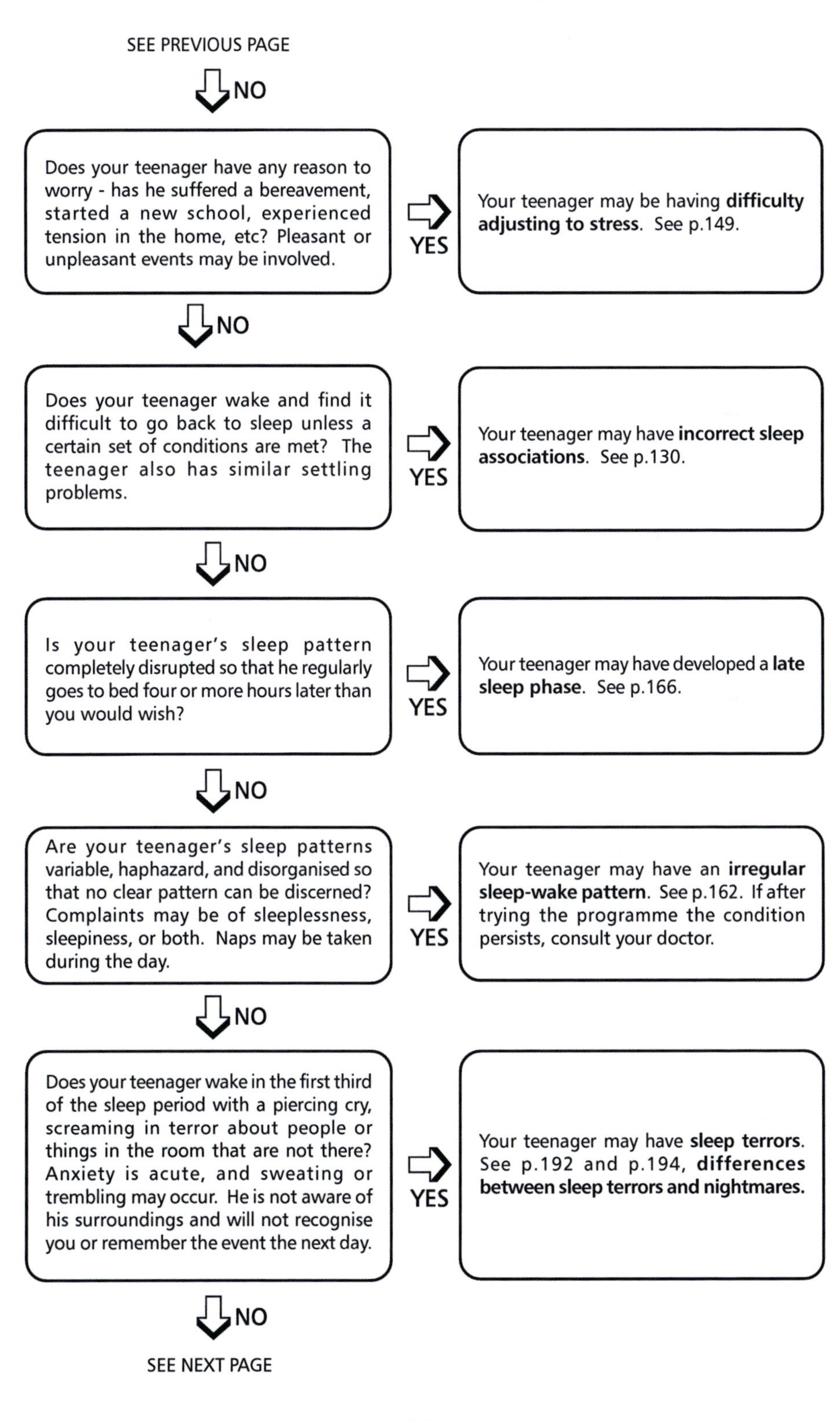
SEE PREVIOUS PAGE
NO
Does your teenager have any reason to worry - has he suffered a bereavement, started a new school, experienced tension in the home, etc? Pleasant or unpleasant events may be involved.
YES
Your teenager may be having **difficulty adjusting to stress**. See p.149.
NO
Does your teenager wake and find it difficult to go back to sleep unless a certain set of conditions are met? The teenager also has similar settling problems.
YES
Your teenager may have **incorrect sleep associations**. See p.130.
NO
Is your teenager's sleep pattern completely disrupted so that he regularly goes to bed four or more hours later than you would wish?
YES
Your teenager may have developed a **late sleep phase**. See p.166.
NO
Are your teenager's sleep patterns variable, haphazard, and disorganised so that no clear pattern can be discerned? Complaints may be of sleeplessness, sleepiness, or both. Naps may be taken during the day.
YES
Your teenager may have an **irregular sleep-wake pattern**. See p.162. If after trying the programme the condition persists, consult your doctor.
NO
Does your teenager wake in the first third of the sleep period with a piercing cry, screaming in terror about people or things in the room that are not there? Anxiety is acute, and sweating or trembling may occur. He is not aware of his surroundings and will not recognise you or remember the event the next day.
YES
Your teenager may have **sleep terrors**. See p.192 and p.194, **differences between sleep terrors and nightmares.**
NO
SEE NEXT PAGE

SEE PREVIOUS PAGE

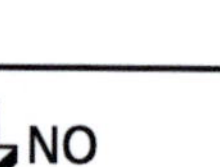

Does your teenager wake in the night feeling frightened and anxious, complaining of nightmares or frightening dreams? These happen in the last third of the sleep period. He will remember the dream in the morning.

YES

Your teenager has probably had a **nightmare**. See p.198 and p.194, **differences between sleep terrors and nightmares.**

NO

If you cannot classify your teenager's problem from this chart, consult your doctor.

Chart 17 Teenagers 13-18 Years

Teenager's sleep is disrupted by events that occur during sleep, sometimes causing waking or partial waking

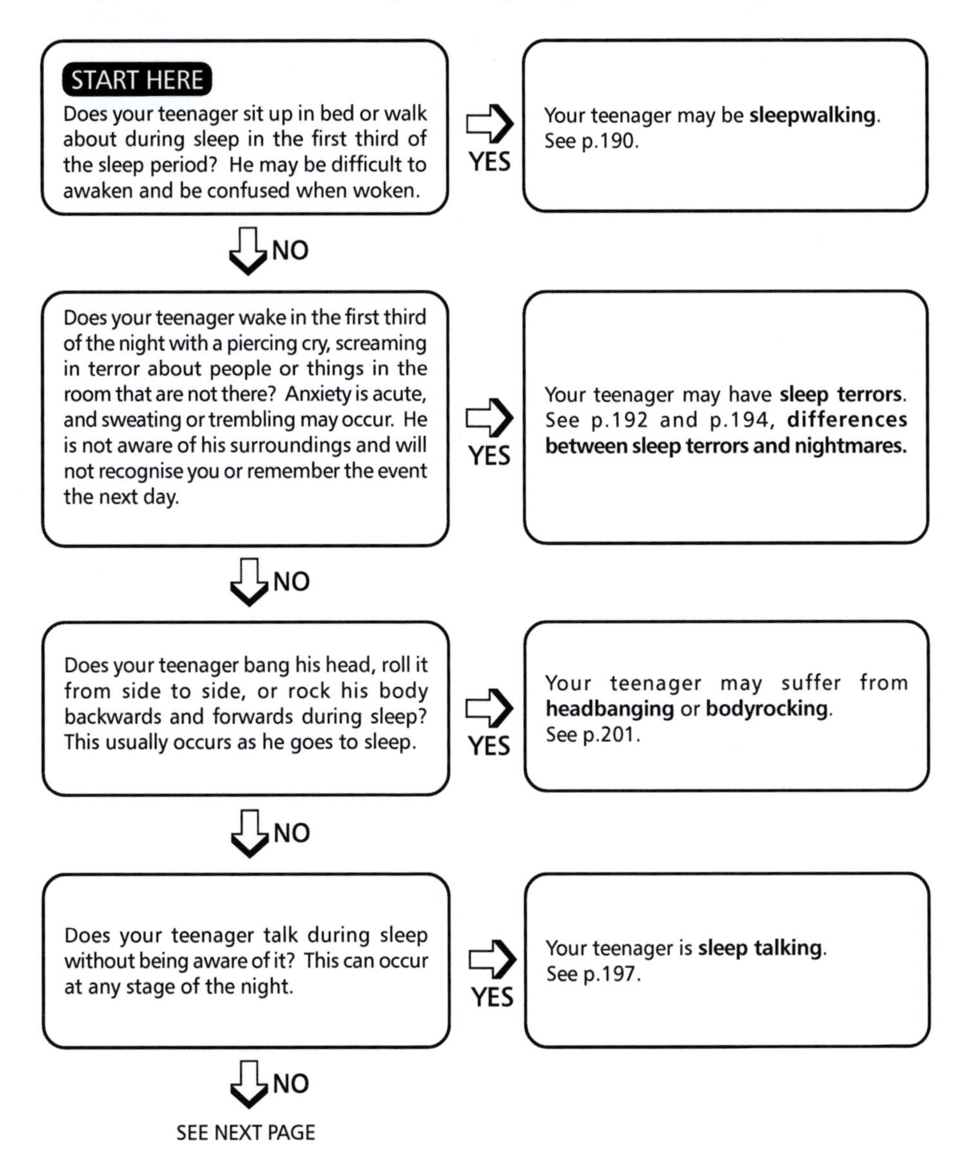

SEE PREVIOUS PAGE

NO

Does your teenager wake in the night feeling frightened and anxious, complaining of nightmares or frightening dreams? These happen in the last third of the sleep period. He will remember the dream in the morning.

YES

Your teenager has probably had a **nightmare**. See p.198, and p.194, **differences between sleep terrors and nightmares.**

Does your teenager grind or clench his teeth during sleep?

Your teenager may have **sleep bruxism**. See p.204.

Does your teenager regularly snore very loudly during sleep and seem to stop breathing for about thirty seconds, suddenly starting again with a raspy snort? Sleep may be disrupted, and the teenager may be very restless in sleep and very sleepy in the daytime.

Your teenager may have **obstructive sleep apnoea**. See p.185. This condition can affect his health and well-being. You should consult your doctor as soon as possible.

If you cannot classify your teenager's problem from this chart, consult your doctor.

PART IV

SOLVING YOUR CHILD'S SLEEP PROBLEM

Advice on How To Carry Out a Programme

This part of the book contains programmes that show you how to improve your child's sleep patterns step by step. The following general guidelines will be useful.

1. Be clear about what the most important problem is.
2. Always carry out the programmes in a way that emphasises your affection and respect for your child.
3. Don't be afraid to set limits to your child's behaviour.
4. Be consistent. Make sure your partner knows what you are doing and is in agreement with you.
5. Always notice and comment on good behaviour.
6. If your child understands, explain what you are doing.
7. Listen carefully to your child.
8. Explain to your child what he should be doing as well as what he should not be doing.
9. Prepare your child for bedtime by developing relaxing routines.
10. Use praise and encouragement frequently.
11. Make sure you are ignoring or penalising unacceptable night-time behaviour.
12. Be persistent!

Talking to Your Child

An important part of managing behaviour is to know how to talk to your child. The way you talk to him teaches him how to talk to other children. Here are some useful tips.

1. Connect with your child before you give a command. Get down to his eye level and engage him in eye to eye contact to get his attention. Ask him to look at you. Do the same when listening to your child.
2. Open your request by using the child's name: 'Jimmy, will you please put on your pyjamas'.
3. Give clear instructions. Use one sentence to communicate your request. The more you say, the more your child is likely to stop listening. Use short sentences with short words.
4. Ask your child to repeat your request back to you.

5. Be positive. Instead of saying 'It's bedtime' try saying 'It's story time'.
6. Try exchanging bad news for good: 'When you have put on your pyjamas, then I'll read you a story'.
7. Give choices: 'Do you want to put on your pyjamas or have a story first?'
8. Give clear warnings that bedtime is approaching. You can do this both by saying to your child 'It will be bedtime soon' and by setting up a bedtime routine in which events follow a logical pattern and end with him being taken to bed, settled, and kissed goodnight.
9. Don't raise your voice. A low, calm voice is best for giving instructions.
10. Make sure the rules are clear. After the bedtime routine, you expect your child to settle quietly to sleep. Make sure he knows what is expected of him.

Some Questions

1. What if my child is sick?

   Do attend to your child's special needs if he is sick by providing medication, extra fluids, or attention during the night. You will need to reintroduce the programme when your child feels better.

2. What happens if my child is teething?

   It is very difficult to know whether a child is crying at night because he is teething. If your child's gums seem red and sore you can help to relieve his discomfort by using a teething gel. Don't stop the programme because of your child's teething.

3. What if my child falls asleep before he is put to bed?

   If this happens, make sure you wake your child so that he knows he is being put to bed. Your child must learn to fall asleep alone, in his own bed.

4. What about the neighbours?

   If you are carrying out a controlled crying or extinction programme, it may help to explain to your neighbours that you are carrying out a programme with your child to establish better sleep patterns.

5. What if my child shares a room?

   If you are unable to change your child's sleeping arrangements so that he sleeps alone you can still carry out the programme. Explain to all the children in the family what is happening so that they will not interfere with the programme by paying attention to their brother after bedtime. They can also join in the praise when the child has had a good night.

6. What if my partner disagrees with what I am doing?

   It is very important that you and your partner talk the matter over and agree on starting a programme. You will need to support each other, particularly during the first few nights. If one party does not agree that a sleep programme should be started it is unlikely to be successful.

7. Will the programmes work for me?

   If you follow the programme carefully and consistently it will work. If you give in part way through or have an inconsistent approach you will reduce the programme's effectiveness.

Advice on How to Settle Your Baby to Sleep

In November 1991 the Department of Health launched 'Back to Sleep', a campaign to reduce cot deaths based on the main risk factors known at the time. The campaign followed publicity on television by Ann Diamond, who had herself lost a baby to cot death. Between 1991 and 1992 the rate of deaths fell by 47% to 0.8 per thousand live births. Provisional figures given by the Government for 1992-3 indicate a further fall of 14%. Thus between 1988 and 1993 there has been a fall of over 70%. However, cot death is still a leading cause of death in babies under a week old.

Below we offer the Government's advice on settling babies to sleep.

❖ Place babies to sleep on their back or side, with the underneath arm brought forward to prevent the child rolling on to the front.

❖ Don't smoke during pregnancy. A mother who smokes 20 or more cigarettes a day increases the baby's risk of cot death by 5 times according to the Foundation for the Study of Infant Death. Babies exposed to smoky atmospheres are also at greater risk.

❖ Don't let the baby get overheated. A room temperature of 18°C is ideal. Remove bedding or clothing if the baby feels hot or is sweating. Don't use a hot water bottle or electric blanket. Make sure that bedding or clothing does not prevent the baby from losing excess heat from his head.

❖ Look out for signs of illness needing medical attention. Emergency treatment is needed if babies stop breathing, turn blue, have glazed eyes and are not focusing, cannot be woken, or have a fit.

Advice about mattresses

In November 1994, anxieties were raised in new and prospective parents by a television programme about cot deaths. The Cook Report suggested that cot death could be linked to the production of toxic gases in mattresses.

The Government responded by announcing an inquiry, to be chaired by Lady Limerick, Vice-Chairwoman of the Foundation for the Study of Infant Death. This has yet to report, although the most recent study on toxic gas in plastic mattresses, from the Public Health Laboratory in Bristol, suggested that the Cook Report research was flawed and that there is no evidence that toxic gases are a cause of sudden infant death. Here is some general advice about mattresses. The most important advice is still to place babies on their backs to sleep and not to smoke near them.

- Mattresses should be firm, clean, well aired, and dry.
- Don't use old or second hand mattresses if you can help it. Do make sure they are well scrubbed and clean.
- If you are still concerned, ask the manufacturers about the flame retardant chemicals used in mattresses before you buy one. Do not buy a mattress that contains phosphorus or stibine (antimony).

Limit Setting Problems*

Limit setting problems occur when parents have felt unable to set consistent bedtime limits. Children become difficult to settle at night, refuse to go to bed at their appropriate bedtime, or occasionally will not go back to bed after night-time wakings. You may find that your child refuses to stay in bed or in the bedroom, and therefore does not stay in bed long enough to fall asleep, even though he is physiologically ready for sleep. He gets out of bed and makes a fuss, you are disturbed, the tension mounts, and you ultimately give in, reinforcing his bad behaviour. Some parents are unaware of the importance of setting bedtime limits, while others are aware that they are not setting adequate limits for the child, but feel unable to enforce appropriate bedtimes. Parents of children with disabilities who have a high level of anxiety about the child frequently find it difficult to set limits for their children.

Sometimes limits are not set at all, and the child simply goes to sleep when he wishes, often in the living room with the parents present and the television on. Both child and parent complain. The child will not go to sleep when the parents desire and usually demands to stay up later. Typically requests are made for a drink or to be tucked in again or for a trip to the bathroom or for a light to be switched on. Sometimes children complain about fears, but these are not usually true fears but ones the child thinks the parents will respond to, such as monsters or robbers. Once the child is old enough to decide on his own bedtime and allow the parents to sleep even if he is not asleep the complaints stop. If the adolescent does not set up appropriate limits for himself the problem becomes either one of **poor sleep hygiene, insufficient sleep**, or **irregular sleep schedules**.

What are the symptoms?

- Delaying bedtime, bedtime battles, or refusing to go to bed at the right time
- Difficulty falling asleep
- Once the child has gone to sleep, sleep is normal

The main feature of this problem is the parents' failure to set limits to bedtime in the face of the child's struggles. Sometimes parents have pressures of their own such as depression or long work hours. Sometimes rows between parents will cause the child to get out of bed to intervene, even at risk of punishment. Some parents may actually enjoy the company of their child at night. Guilt may be a problem, particularly for parents of a child born with disability or other medical problems or a child who was

*The name given to this disorder in the International Classification of Sleep Disorders is 'limit setting sleep disorder'.

premature or has been in hospital. It is sometimes difficult to stand up to the pleading requests of such children.

How common is it?

About 10% of children are said to suffer from this problem. Children with learning disabilities are particularly prone to it because it is often more difficult for them to learn what is expected of them at bedtime. Some individuals tend to be 'night owls'. Such children are more likely to try to stay up late.

When does it start?

The problem is not usually seen before the child is capable of making verbal demands — ie at about two years of age. It is more common when the child is able to climb out of his cot or is moved to a bed, at about three years. However, this problem can occur at any point from late infancy through to adolescence and sometimes becomes chronic.

How long does it last?

The problem can last a long or a short time, depending upon the reasons why parents fail to set limits. If these factors can be resolved, sleep problems will usually disappear.

Does my child have a limit setting problem?

Your child probably has a limit setting problem if

❖ there is difficulty in falling asleep.

❖ there is refusal to go to bed at an appropriate time or bedtime battles.

❖ once sleep has started it is normal.

❖ there is no evidence of any other medical condition that will account for the complaint.

Other problems to consider are **late sleep phase**, an inappropriately early bedtime (see p.24), **incorrect sleep associations**, **anxieties or night-time fears**, **irregular sleep-wake patterns**, and the **effects of medication**. With an inappropriately early bedtime or late sleep phase the child falls asleep at the same time each night, regardless of bedtime and degree to which limits are set. This distinguishes these problems from limit setting problems. An anxious child wants your presence, and if you stay with the child sleep will come quickly without continued demands. Irregular sleep-wake patterns or the effects of medication may lead to bedtime struggles, but here too sleep will be slow to come even if limits are firmly set.

What can I do about it?

There are six programmes that you can use to deal with limit setting problems and teach your child new bedtime rules without having a major confrontation. Programme 1 can be used to get your child to bed and to encourage him to settle quietly. It is a graded steps programme coupled with positive routines and positive reinforcement. Programme 2 is a programme for children who get out of bed or come downstairs repeatedly after being put to bed. It is a graded steps programme which uses positive reinforcement. Programme 3 can be used for the child whose bedtime has got later and later, but who still requires a graded approach. Programme 4 can be used if your child comes downstairs or gets into your bed. It is an extinction programme, but you can couple it with positive reinforcement. Programme 5 will help you to bring your child's bedtime forward to a more suitable time. It is a faded bedtime procedure. Programme 6 uses positive reinforcement and can be used for all limit setting problems. You can use it in combination with many of the other programmes. The programmes can also be combined with Programme 8 to correct your child's sleep associations if he will not go to sleep alone in his own bed, or needs to be rocked or cuddled to sleep.

If your child has had this problem for a long time, his sleep cycle may have shifted so that he naturally falls asleep later in the evening than you would like (see page 166). You can gradually reschedule your child's sleep cycle at the same time as dealing with the limit setting problem by using the methods described in Programmes 3, 5, 18 and 19.

Programme 1

Use this programme if your child is difficult to settle at night and there are bedtime battles. It is a graded steps programme coupled with positive routines and positive reinforcement.

Step 1 Decide on an appropriate bedtime. Once you have decided on a reasonable time, don't vary it. A consistent bedtime will help to establish regular sleep patterns.

Step 2 Start a regular, relaxing bedtime routine (see page 66). The routine should be a comforting time alone with one parent to help your child to unwind and prepare for sleep. Begin the routine at a set bedtime, follow the same sequence of events, and allow it to take 20-30 minutes each night.

Step 3 Once you have finished your bedtime routine, say goodnight and leave the bedroom.

Step 4 Allow your child to cry or call out for gradually longer periods of time before going in to check. The chart below shows you how to do this.

First, when the child starts to cry, call out, or have a tantrum, wait 5 minutes before going in to comfort her. After 5 minutes, go into the bedroom, comfort and resettle her quickly, and leave the bedroom even if she is still having a tantrum. If your child leaves her bed, return her to the bed and say firmly 'Go to sleep'. Spend only a short time — 1-2 minutes at most. You are only going in to reassure her and yourself, not to help her fall asleep. The goal is for her to fall asleep alone. Make sure you leave the room while she is still awake.

Do not cuddle, talk to, or sit with your child. Simply check that she is alright and leave the room. Deal gently but firmly with her.

Step 5 If your child cries for a further 10 minutes repeat the intervention.

Step 6 If she is still crying or having a tantrum after a quarter of an hour, return again.

Step 7 15 minutes is the maximum for the first night. If your child is still crying or having a tantrum, continue waiting for 15 minute periods, checking briefly in between, until she falls asleep during one of these periods.

Repeat if the child wakes again and cries during the night, starting with a 5 minute wait.

Step 8 Each night increase the waiting time as shown in the chart.

Make sure your child falls asleep while you are not in the room.

If your child is old enough, you can try a reward system to help the new learning progress more quickly. Make sure you apply the rules for rewards given on page 63. Reward your child the next morning after she has settled well.

Be sure to follow the schedule carefully and record your child's sleep patterns in the diary given on page 7 so you can monitor her progress.

Step 9 The programme will probably take a week to ten days. If further days are necessary, add 5 minutes to each time on successive days.

NB If your child has had this problem for a long time, her sleep cycle may have shifted so that she naturally falls asleep later in the evening than you would like (see page 166). You can reschedule her sleep cycle by using the method described in Programmes 18 and 19.

Number of Minutes to Wait Before Checking Briefly on Your Child

Day	1	2	3	4	5	6	7	8	9	10
First check	5	10	15	20	25	30	35	40	45	50
If your child is still crying										
Second check	10	15	20	25	30	35	40	45	50	55
Third check	15	20	25	30	35	40	45	50	55	60
Subsequent checks	15	20	25	30	35	40	45	50	55	60

Programme 2

This is a programme for children who get out of bed or come downstairs repeatedly after being put to bed. The programme starts with a positive routine and then uses graded steps with positive reinforcement.

Step 1 Explain to your child if he is old enough and can understand that you are going to have new rules at bedtime.

Step 2 Start a bedtime routine: story, quiet talk and cuddle, settle your child into bed and say goodnight.

Step 3 When you hear the child get out of bed, or if he comes downstairs, go back into the room, resettle him, and tell him he must stay in bed or you will close the door.

Step 4 If he gets out of bed again, resettle him and close the door for 1 minute. Hold it closed if necessary. You want him to learn that having the door open is under his control — if he stays in bed the door will be left open, if he gets out of bed the door will be closed.

You may talk to the child through the closed door. If he is able to understand, tell him that you will leave the door open after the minute is up if he gets back into bed. If he does not, go in yourself, put him into bed, and close the door. Wait 2 minutes. If he continues to get out, close the door for 3 minutes, increasing to 5 (see chart). 5 minutes is the maximum for the first night.

Step 5 Keep the door closed for the number of minutes listed even if he goes back to bed earlier. When you open the door, speak to him briefly. If he is in bed, praise him and leave. If he is still out of bed, remind him of the rules, put him back to bed, and shut the door for the next amount of time listed below. If you can put him back to bed easily and you think he will stay there, you can try leaving the door open, but if he gets out of bed do not make the same mistake twice.

Step 6 When the child finally stays in bed or goes back to bed on his own, open the door when the time is up and praise him. Do not go into the room.

Step 7 If he gets up following night wakings, follow the same routine.

Step 8 On the second night, start with 2 minutes' door closing and increase each night. If he wakes and cries but stays in bed, switch to the routine of waiting longer before you respond.

Give plenty of praise the next morning each time your child settles easily. You can also try other rewards (see pages 62-64). Do this in a consistent way.

Be sure to follow the schedule carefully and record your child's sleep patterns every day so you can monitor his progress.

Number of Minutes to Close the Door if Your Child Will Not Stay in Bed

Day	1	2	3	4	5	6	7	8	9	10	11
First time	1	2	3	4	5	7	10	15	20	25	30
If your child continues trying to get out of bed											
Second time	2	4	5	6	7	10	15	20	25	30	35
Third time	3	6	7	8	10	15	20	25	30	35	40
Fourth time	5	8	10	12	15	20	25	30	35	40	45
Subsequent checks	5	8	10	12	15	20	25	30	35	40	45

Programme 3

This is another graded steps programme that you can use if your child is unwilling to go to sleep when put to bed and her bedtime has become later than you desire. This programme will teach your child new sleep associations — to fall asleep alone. You can also use it when your child wakes up in the night and wants you to go to her. It is particularly suitable for parents who find it hard to leave the child to cry even for a few minutes.

Step 1 Start a regular, relaxing bedtime routine half an hour earlier than the time your child has become used to going to bed. It should include four or five activities such as giving your child a bath, putting her into pyjamas, playing music or reading a story. The routine will help her relax and unwind, ready to go to sleep. Begin the routine at the same time each night and allow about half an hour per night.

Step 2 Once the routine is complete, say goodnight. Your goal is now to distance yourself gradually from your child's room in a series of steps which will take a few days to complete. She must learn some new bedtime rules, and at first she won't understand them. She should know that you are still near and taking care of her. If you plan a progressive approach your child will learn what you have in mind in an easier way. You will still be around and responsive to her, and you will not need to worry that she might cry until she becomes ill. As you gradually distance yourself from her room your child will learn to anticipate this. It is very difficult to listen to several hours' crying night after night, and an older child will very likely cry constantly or intermittently for an hour or more. The longer she cries, the more likely you will be to change your mind and go to her, so the crying doesn't help. Better sleep will come when the child learns how to go to sleep and return to sleep alone. The progressive approach means that you and your partner will not argue about it and undermine each other.

Step 3 On the first night of the programme, after the bedtime routine, sit rather than lying down on the child's bed until she goes to sleep. Resist attempts by the child to persuade you to lie down on the bed.

Repeat this on the subsequent 2-3 nights, until the child tolerates it without fuss. Allow her to go to sleep before you leave the room. When she has accepted this step, proceed to Step 4.

Step 4 Instead of sitting on the bed, place a chair beside it. Sit on the chair, perhaps touching the child. Do this for 2-3 nights, until she tolerates this without fuss. Allow her to fall asleep before you leave the room. Then proceed to Step 5.

Step 5 Sit by the bed, not touching the child. Do this for 2-3 nights, allowing her to fall asleep before you leave the room. When she tolerates this without fuss proceed to Step 6.

Step 6 Sit at gradually increasing distances from the child's bed. You must decide how many steps to take. Each time you move the chair, leave it in the same spot for 2-3 nights. As each step is established you can move your chair gradually towards the door.

Step 7 Eventually, place the chair outside the bedroom door. Sit on the chair until the child falls asleep. Do this for 2-3 nights.

Step 8 When the child tolerates this stage without fuss, you can take the chair away and enjoy your evening.

Your response when your child wakes in the night should reflect the stage you are at in the settling routine.

Each week that you carry out the graded steps routine, begin the routine 15 minutes earlier until the child is going to bed at the time you desire.

After you have said goodnight, do not talk to or play with your child. If you have to stop her from playing around, use a firm voice to say her name and give a simple, direct command, such as 'Go to sleep'. Otherwise, try not to establish eye contact with the child or to smile at her. You are not there to keep her company or talk to her. You are simply there to reassure her and to ensure that she comes to no harm while falling asleep.

Give generous praise the next morning each time the child settles easily. You can also try other rewards. Do this in a consistent way (see pages 62-64).

Fill in a sleep diary every night to monitor your child's progress.

Programme 4

This is an alternative programme for children who keep coming downstairs or who get into your bed during the night. It is an extinction programme, but you can couple it with positive reinforcement.

Step 1 Decide on an appropriate bedtime. Once you have decided on a reasonable time, don't vary it. A consistent bedtime will help establish a regular sleep-wake rhythm.

Step 2 Start a regular, relaxing bedtime routine (see page 66). The routine should be a comforting time alone with one parent to help your child unwind and prepare for sleep. Begin the routine at the set bedtime, follow the same sequence of events, and allow it to take about 20-30 minutes each night.

Step 3 Once you have finished your bedtime routine, say goodnight and leave the bedroom before your child is asleep.

You can help your child to learn to settle to sleep easily by giving him his favourite teddy bear or toy to cuddle.

Step 4 When your child comes downstairs or creeps into your bed during the night, take him back to bed, resettle him, and leave him to go to sleep.

Do this as often as he comes downstairs or gets into your bed, until he falls asleep in his own bed.

Do not become hostile, scream, or punish the child. Do not feel guilty. You have given your child plenty of attention at bedtime.

Do not sympathise, hug or cuddle your child, or show any distress.

Be firm and give a simple, direct command such as 'Go to sleep'.

By the end of a week, your child should stay in bed and fall asleep alone. If the programme takes longer, do not worry. Do not give in, or else the behaviour will get worse again.

Step 5 In the morning when your child has stayed in bed, give him lots of praise, cuddles, and hugs.

Be sure to follow the schedule carefully and record you child's sleep patterns in the diary on page 7 so you can monitor his progress.

Programme 5

Try this programme if your child has settling problems that result in her falling asleep much later than you wish or if she suffers from excessive sleepiness during the day. It will help to bring her bedtime forward to a more suitable time.

Step 1 Use the chart on page 16 to work out the average number of hours of sleep needed by your child. Then calculate 'ideal' sleep and wake times. For example, if your child is aged about 3 years she will need about 12 hours' sleep. If you put her to bed at 7pm she should wake at about 7am. This will be your goal.

Step 2 Collect some baseline measures. For one week carry out the child's normal bedtime routine, but instead of insisting that she goes to bed simply prompt her to go to bed every 30 minutes. For each day write down the time she eventually goes to bed. If you have to put her to bed because she cannot take herself, wait until she is falling asleep before you do this. This may be within half an hour of her normal bedtime or it may be up to 2 hours after it. Do this every day for a week.

Step 3 Use the baseline information to decide on a bedtime at which your child will go to sleep quickly (within 15 minutes). This is how to do it. Calculate the average time at which she went to sleep each night the previous week, and then add 30 minutes (eg if the average time of going to sleep was 10.30pm during the baseline period, set a bedtime of 11pm for the first night of the programme).

Step 4 **Days 1 & 2** Don't let the child fall asleep or go to bed before the bedtime you have calculated or sleep past the wake time (eg if she goes to bed at 10pm and needs 10 hours' sleep, don't let her sleep beyond 8am the following morning). Make a note of the time she goes to sleep.

Step 5 **Day 3** Now you can begin to 'fade' the child's bedtime. For the third night you have to adjust her bedtime according to how quickly she went to sleep on the previous two nights. If she went to sleep within 15 minutes of bedtime on both nights, make the bedtime 15 minutes earlier on the third night. If she did not go to sleep within 15 minutes of bedtime on both nights, make the bedtime 15 minutes later on the third night.

Step 6 **Day 5 onwards** If your child falls asleep within 15 minutes of the new bedtime two nights in a row, make her bedtime 15 minutes earlier on the third night. If she does not, make her bedtime 15 minutes later. Continue this procedure until the desired bedtime has been reached.

Programme 6

This programme is based on positive reinforcement (reward) and is very effective. As we noted in Part II, behaviour that is rewarded will continue, while behaviour that is unrewarded will cease. Star charts are a way to encourage your child towards goals you have set for him by providing an incentive. You arrange for him to earn a reward — a star or sticker — for good/desirable behaviour. These charts work well because the child is able to see his daily progress towards a reward. You can combine it with the other programmes. This programme can be used if your child is 3 or over. We have used an example of a child who gets out of bed, but you can use the programme to encourage any appropriate night-time behaviour.

Step 1 Explain to your child that you want to help him to stay in bed at night and that you are going to use a star chart. With your child's help, make a chart from white card, marking on it the days of the week. You will find one to copy on the next page. You will need to buy one packet of red stars and one of gold stars or two different types of sticker from a stationer's.

Step 2 Each time your child stays in his own bed *all* night, give him a red star.

Step 3 When he spends three nights in a row in his own bed, award him a gold star.

Encourage your child to stick the stars on the chart himself and always accompany the sticking with praise. Encourage your partner to join in the praise.

Put the chart in a prominent position where it can be seen easily. This will act as a frequent reminder of the desired behaviour and allow your child to proudly show his progress.

Ignore nights when your child gets out of bed or cries and screams for attention. Don't make a fuss, but don't give him a star.

Step 4 Continue the chart until the child has had four weeks in which he has not got out of bed.

You can add to the reinforcement by giving your child a small toy or reward of his choice for every two or three gold stars. When your child's behaviour begins to improve you can gradually increase the number of gold stars required to earn a reward.

Keep the time until the reward is collected short. A week is long enough. Frequent rewards keep motivation high.

Never give a star if the child has not complied with your request to stay in bed.

Instead of stars you can use any kind of sticker the child enjoys, such as dinosaurs, trolls, or boglins.

STAR CHART

NAME...

	Monday	Tuesday	Wednesday	Thursday	Friday	Saturday	Sunday
Week 1 **Date:**							
Week 2 **Date:**							
Week 3 **Date:**							
Week 4 **Date:**							
Week 5 **Date:**							

Incorrect Sleep Associations*

One of the most common causes of children's waking problems is incorrect sleep associations. These occur when going to sleep is delayed by the absence of a certain object or set of circumstances. When certain conditions are met, such as the mother lying down with the child, sleep is normal, but when they are not, going to sleep at bedtime and returning to sleep after night waking are delayed.

All children wake up or come close to waking several times in the night. Most children learn to roll over and put themselves back to sleep. Return to sleep is usually swift and the child does not even remember the short wakening. If there are any changes in the sleeping environment, however, it may be difficult for the child to return to sleep and he may wake up fully. Falling asleep is a complex business. First your child's body must be physiologically ready for sleep. Second a series of bedtime 'rituals' usually follow. You may adjust his pillows, tuck him in, and give him a cuddly toy or a special blanket. A night light may be switched on. You may rock him to sleep or lie down on his bed until he drifts off. Without these associations or behavioural rituals, falling off to sleep may be difficult or impossible for the child. We learn to fall asleep in a particular way and this learned behaviour is repeated every night. When the associations are present sleep is normal, but when they are absent sleep is disturbed, and this can result both in difficulties settling to sleep and frequent night waking. If you have got into a habit of rocking your child to sleep, allowing him to fall asleep downstairs, or lying down on his bed with him, he may not be able to fall asleep without these learned associations.

The usual complaint made by parents of children who have formed the wrong sleep associations is night waking. Such children are not difficult to settle at night because the associations they need to settle to sleep are present. The problem starts when the child wakes up to find there is no-one there. He will wake frequently in the night and cry noisily until you go into his bedroom. The child will settle again quite easily if you then provide him with the correct sleep associations (rocking, cuddling, lying down on the bed). He needs to learn to fall asleep at bedtime with the same associations that will be present when he wakes at night.

*Sleep onset association disorder.

What are the symptoms?

- Frequent prolonged night wakings
- The problem is associated with the absence of certain conditions, eg being held, rocked, or breast fed, having the parent in the bedroom, or falling asleep in the parents' bed or downstairs. The child wakes up and the conditions usually associated with falling asleep are not present
- Settling is not a problem provided that the associations required for sleep are present
- Parents may become chronically sleep deprived because of the child's wakings

How common is it?

Approximately 15-20% in children aged 0-3 years. Studies have found that up to 50% of children with learning disabilities may experience this problem.

Any event or upheaval can trigger this problem. Sometimes it may follow a period of illness or pain that has required the parent to give extra attention to the child. The child may have been a colicky baby, needing to be carried about or rocked in the evening, or may have had recurring ear infections or discomfort due to muscle spasm or physical disability. Various sleep associations may start during difficult periods in the child's life. Once learned, they persist even after the original difficulties, illness, or pain have disappeared. Temperamental factors may also be important. Some children are better able to calm themselves and fall asleep than others, and these children seem more resistant to developing unhelpful sleep associations.

Sometimes parents unintentionally play a part in the development of the problem. Parents of a child who has suffered medical problems or hospitalisation early on may be more protective and more anxious. They may respond more readily to the child when he makes the slightest noise.

When does it start?

Since children are not expected to sleep through the night regularly until about six months of age it is not usually diagnosed in the early months. It may start at any time during late infancy and early childhood.

How long does it last?

This is mainly a problem of early childhood, when the conditions associated with sleep require the parents' help to become established. Later on the associations come under the control of the young person himself. However, it is a problem frequently found at older ages in children with physical or mental handicap.

Does my child have incorrect sleep associations?

Your child probably has incorrect sleep associations if

- ❖ he wakes frequently during the night.
- ❖ the complaint is associated with the absence of certain conditions when he wakes in the night, eg being held, rocked, or nursed while falling asleep.
- ❖ there is no problem going to sleep at bedtime so long as these conditions are met.
- ❖ sleep is normal if the associations are present.
- ❖ the problem has been present for at least three weeks.
- ❖ there is no evidence of a medical disorder that can account for the symptoms.

Other problems to consider are **limit setting problems**, **late sleep phase**, **difficulty adjusting to stress**, **irregular sleep-wake patterns**, and **insufficient sleep**. Limit setting problems and late sleep phase usually only produce bedtime battles, not night waking. Pain from medical conditions, difficulty adjusting to stress, irregular sleep-wake patterns, and insufficient sleep also produce multiple wakings, but in these cases parental intervention does not result in rapid return to sleep even if the conditions associated with sleep are re-established.

What can I do about about it?

We offer four programmes to help you correct your child's sleep associations. Programme 7 is a graded steps programme. It is a controlled crying programme that will help your child learn to fall asleep with new associations — alone, in his own bed. Programme 8 is a programme for parents who have had to lie down with their child or stay in the bedroom until he falls asleep. If you find it difficult to leave your child to cry even for a few minutes, this is the programme to use. It will teach your child to fall asleep alone. It is a graded steps programme in which you gradually distance yourself from the child's room. Programme 9 is for children who wake and get out of bed, or disturb the parents' night by coming downstairs or getting into their parents' bed. This programme uses a graded steps approach with positive reinforcement. Programme 10 is an extinction programme for children who wake at night and come downstairs or get into their parents' bed. It will do the same job as Programme 9, but will work faster. However, you must only attempt an extinction programme if you are brave enough to cope with the extra crying and temper tantrums that it will produce at first.

Programme 7

The following graded steps programme will help your child to learn to fall asleep with new associations — alone in his own bed. Then when he wakes at night, instead of crying and disturbing you, he will just turn over and go back to sleep. The programme uses a graded steps controlled crying approach to teach your child some new rules about bedtime. You can also use positive reinforcement to help him learn more quickly (see Programme 6 and pages 62-64). The programme can be used for all children from a year old.

Step 1 Explain to your child if he is old enough and able to understand that you can no longer lie down/cuddle/rock him while he falls asleep.

Step 2 Set up a pleasant bedtime routine. When you finish the story, talk, or music tape, tuck your child in, say goodnight, and leave the room, leaving the door open. If your child simply calls out or cries, follow the routine below. If he gets out of bed or comes downstairs you will need a different approach. You will find this in Programmes 9 and 10.

At bedtime, or after any night waking, the child must be allowed to fall asleep alone, in his own bed.

Step 3 If the child wakes and grizzles a little but does not really cry, don't interfere. Remember most children wake up in the night several times. It is best to leave the child who is not really crying to settle himself and go back to sleep. If you go in you will only arouse him fully.

Step 4 Allow the child to cry for gradually longer periods of time before going in to check on him. The chart below shows you how to do this.

First check briefly if he is still crying after 5 minutes. This will reassure him (and you) that he is really alright. Spend only a short time — 2-3 minutes at most. You are only going in to reassure him and yourself, not to help him to stop crying or to fall asleep. The goal is for him to fall asleep alone. Make sure you leave the room while he is still awake.

Do not talk to, cuddle, or sit with your child. Simply check he is alright and leave the room. Deal gently but firmly with him.

Step 5 If the child cries for a further 10 minutes, repeat the intervention.

Step 6 If he is still crying after a quarter of an hour, return again.

Step 7 15 minutes is the maximum for the first night. If the child is still crying, continue waiting for 15 minute periods, checking briefly, until he falls asleep during one of these periods.

Repeat if the child wakes again and cries during the night, starting with a 5 minute wait.

Step 8 Each night, increase the waiting time as shown in the chart.

Make sure the child falls asleep while you are not in the room.

If your child is old enough (over 3) you can try a reward system to help the new learning go faster. Make sure you apply the rules for rewards given on page 63.

Be sure to follow the schedule carefully and record your child's sleep patterns in the diary given on page 7 so you can monitor his progress. Be firm and carry on for as long as is necessary. There is no point in starting this programme unless you are prepared to see it through.

Step 9 The programme will probably take about a week to ten days. If further days are necessary, just continue to add 5 minutes to each time on successive days.

Often parents say that they have tried leaving their child to cry but it does not work. I usually find that the child has been left to cry for a while but has not been left to fall asleep. The point of this programme is to teach your child new associations for going to sleep — how to return to sleep on his own without your presence. Your child will not understand these rules at first, so it is better to use this gradual approach so that he knows you are still there and caring for him. As you gradually increase the time before you go in, he will quickly recognise what is happening. He may try crying even harder to get you to change your mind, but he will gradually learn that it is not worth crying for 15 minutes just to get you to come in to him briefly, and he will learn to fall asleep alone.

Number of Minutes to Wait Before Checking Briefly on Your Child

Day	**1**	**2**	**3**	**4**	**5**	**6**	**7**	**8**	**9**	**10**
First check	5	10	15	20	25	30	35	40	45	50
If your child is still crying										
Second check	10	15	20	25	30	35	40	45	50	55
Third check	15	20	25	30	35	40	45	50	55	60
Subsequent checks	15	20	25	30	35	40	45	50	55	60

Programme 8

This is another programme for parents whose child has waking problems because of incorrect sleep associations. This programme will teach your child new sleep associations — to fall asleep alone. You can also use it when your child wakes up in the night and wants you to go to her. It is particularly suitable for parents who find it hard to leave the child to cry even for a few minutes. It is a graded steps programme.

Step 1 Decide on an appropriate bedtime. Once you have decided on a reasonable time, don't vary it. A consistent bedtime will help your child establish a regular sleep-wake rhythm.

Step 2 Start a regular, relaxing bedtime routine, such as giving a bath, putting your child into pyjamas, playing music or reading a story. The routine will help her relax and unwind, ready to go to sleep. Begin the routine at a set time each night and allow about half an hour per night.

Step 3 Once the routine is complete, say goodnight to the child. Your goal is now to distance yourself gradually from her room in a series of steps which will take a few days to complete. You could of course simply leave the room and allow her to 'cry it out'. Indeed, friends and relatives may have recommended this strategy to you. The method would certainly work. You could also use Programme 7, which is a controlled crying approach. However, sometimes parents want to use an even more gradual approach. Your child must learn some new bedtime rules, and at first she won't understand them. She should know that you are still near and taking care of her. If you plan a progressive approach your child will learn what you have in mind in an easier way. You will still be around and responsive to her. And you will not need to worry that she might cry until she becomes ill. As you gradually distance yourself from her room your child will learn to anticipate this. It is very difficult to listen to several hours' crying night after night, and an older child will very likely cry constantly or intermittently for an hour or more. The longer she cries, the more likely you will be to change your mind and go to her, so the crying doesn't help. Better sleep will come when the child learns how to go to sleep and return to sleep alone. The progressive approach means that you and your husband will not argue about it and undermine each other.

Use this routine both to settle your child to sleep and teach her new sleep associations, and gradually to reduce your responsiveness when your child wakes in the night.

Step 4 On the first night of the programme, after the bedtime routine, sit rather than lying down on your child's bed until she goes to sleep. Resist attempts by the child to persuade you to lie down on the bed.

Repeat this on the subsequent 2-3 nights, until the child tolerates it without fuss. Allow her to go to sleep before you leave the room. When she has accepted this step, proceed to Step 5.

Step 5 Instead of sitting on the bed, place a chair beside it. Sit on the chair, perhaps touching the child. Do this for 2-3 nights, until she tolerates this without fuss. Allow her to fall asleep before you leave the room. Then proceed to Step 6.

Step 6 Sit by the bed, not touching the child. Do this for 2-3 nights, allowing her to fall asleep before you leave the room. When she tolerates this without fuss proceed to Step 7.

Step 7 Sit at gradually increasing distances from the child's bed. You must decide how many steps to take. Each time you move the chair, leave it in the same spot for 2-3 nights. As each step is established you can move your chair gradually towards the door.

Step 8 Eventually, place the chair outside the bedroom door. Sit on the chair until the child falls asleep. Do this for 2-3 nights.

Step 9 When the child tolerates this stage without fuss, you can take the chair away and enjoy your evening.

Your response when your child wakes in the night should reflect the stage you are at in the settling routine.

You can help your child to learn to put herself back to sleep. When you attend to her, give her her favourite teddy bear or toy to cuddle. Use the same association when settling her to sleep. Place the teddy in her arms and let her settle to sleep, so that if she does wake up the teddy can substitute for your presence.

After you have said goodnight, do not talk to or play with your child. If you have to stop her from playing around, use a firm voice to say her name and give a simple, direct command, such as 'Go to sleep'. Otherwise, try not to establish eye contact with the child or to smile at her. You are not there to keep her company or talk to her. You are simply there to reassure her and to ensure that she comes to no harm while falling asleep.

Give generous praise the next morning each time the child settles easily. You can also try other rewards. Do this in a consistent way (see pages 62-64).

Fill in a sleep diary every night to monitor your child's progress.

Programme 9

This is a programme for children who wake and get out of bed or disturb the parents' night by coming downstairs or getting into their parents' bed. The goal is the same as for Programme 8: your child is waking because the conditions she associates with falling asleep are not present at night-time wakings. She must learn to fall asleep with the same associations that are present when she wakes in the night — alone and in bed. This programme uses a graded steps approach, with positive reinforcement.

Step 1 Explain to your child if she is old enough and can understand that you are going to have new rules at bedtime.

Step 2 Start a bedtime routine: story, quiet talk and cuddle, settle the child into bed and say goodnight.

Step 3 When you hear the child get out of bed, or if she comes downstairs, go back into the room, resettle her, and tell her she must stay in bed or you will close the door.

Step 4 If your child gets out of bed again, resettle her and close the door for 1 minute. Hold it closed if necessary. You want her to learn that having the door open is under her control — if she stays in bed the door will be left open, if she gets out of bed the door will be closed.

You may talk to your child through the closed door. If she is able to understand, tell her that you will leave the door open after the minute is up if she gets back into bed. If she does not, go in yourself, put her into bed, and close the door. Wait 2 minutes. If she continues to get out, close the door for 3 minutes, increasing to 5 (see chart on p.124). 5 minutes is maximum for the first night.

Step 5 Keep the door closed for the number of minutes listed even if she goes back to bed earlier. When you open the door, speak to her briefly. If she is in bed, praise her and leave. If she is still out of bed, remind her of the rules, put her back to bed, and shut the door for the next amount of time listed below. If you can put her back to bed easily and you think she will stay there, you can try leaving the door open, but if she gets out of bed do not make the same mistake twice.

Step 6 When your child finally stays in bed or goes back to bed on her own, open the door when the time is up and praise her. Do not go into the room.

Step 7 If she gets up following night wakings, follow the same routine.

Step 8 On the second night, start with 2 minutes' door closing and increase each night as shown in the chart. If she wakes and cries but stays in bed, change to the routine of waiting longer before you respond (see page 133).

Be sure to follow the schedule carefully and record your child's sleep patterns every day so you can monitor her progress.

Your goal is to help your child learn to go to sleep alone. You use the door as a controlled way to enforce this, not to frighten or punish her. Reassure her by talking through the door. Don't scold the child or shout at her. With a graded steps approach, your child does not have to be shut behind a closed door unsure of when it will open. She will learn that having the door open is under her control.

Step 9 By Day 10 or 11 your child will probably be staying in bed. If further days are necessary, continue to add 5 minutes to each time on successive days.

Programme 10

This programme is also suitable for children who wake at night and either come downstairs or repeatedly get into their parents' bed. It will solve the problem faster than Programme 9, but it is harder to carry out because it will initially result in an increase in difficult behaviour.

Step1 Explain to your child if he is old enough and can understand that you are going to have new rules at bedtime.

Step 2 Start a bedtime routine: story, quiet talk and a cuddle, settle the child into bed and say goodnight.

Step 3 When the child wakes and comes downstairs or gets into your bed, take him back to bed, resettle him, say goodnight firmly, and leave the room decisively as though you mean it. Do not rise to requests for cuddles or stories.

Step 4 Do this as often as he comes downstairs/gets into your bed. You must be firm. You have given him plenty of attention before bedtime, so do not feel guilty.

Do not become hostile or scream or shout at your child. Be firm. Make it clear that you are in charge and you do not expect to be disturbed again.

Do not sympathise, hug or cuddle your child. He has to learn that bedtime is a time for sleeping. Give a simple, direct command 'Go to sleep' and leave.

If you are very tired you must be very determined to resist the temptation to let the child stay in your bed. Giving in only reinforces his undesirable behaviour.

Your child may give up getting out of bed and cry quite hard instead at first in an attempt to get you to relent. It's better if you can ignore this crying, but if you feel you have to go in and check he is alright, make this as brief as possible. Go on to a gradual routine, waiting a few more minutes each time before you check on him.

Step 5 By the end of the week your child should be staying in bed. If the programme takes longer or your child stops coming out of the bedroom but stays in bed crying, do not worry. Simply change to the routine described on page 133 of waiting a little longer between checks.

In the morning, when your child has stayed in bed, give him lots of attention, praise, and cuddles.

Be sure to follow the schedule carefully and record your child's sleep patterns in the diary on page 7 so you can monitor his progress.

Anxieties or Night-Time Fears

Many children suffer from anxieties or night-time fears at some time. Frequently they are related to the child's age and stage of physical and emotional development. The very young child may suffer anxiety about separation from his parents, or may be disturbed by feelings of rivalry with brothers and sisters or a new baby, or may fear death or the loss of a parent. The older child may be upset by a frightening video or television programme. Scenes of violence can seem very real to a child and make it difficult for him to relax and go to sleep. Stress in the family, such as illness, divorce, marital quarrels, or death may lead to worry, anxiety, or guilt, which emerge as night-time fears or frightening dreams. Teenagers, too, often have many fears and anxieties as they experience the physical and emotional changes at puberty. Some children seem to be more anxious than others and prone to night-time fears.

It is much more difficult for a child to deal with his fears at night-time. During the day activities keep him busy. There is no time to worry about problems. But at night as your child goes to bed or when he wakes, he has time to think about his fears and anxiety and it is harder to keep them under control. Anxieties or night-time fears can show up as settling or waking problems. The child may complain of robbers, monsters, or frightening dreams. Sometimes children play a game of being frightened at night — they will tell their parents that there is a monster in the cupboard which will eat them up once the parent has gone, for example. Most parents can tell the difference between a really fearful child and a child who is simply trying to get bedtime postponed.

This is what one parent said about her child's night-time fears.

My three-year-old son has always been a good sleeper, going to bed in his own room and sleeping through. Just recently he has refused to go to bed, getting quite hysterical when I leave the room and running downstairs. In the night he sleeps for a few hours, then runs into our room in a terrible state, refusing to go back to bed. I have also noticed a change in his behaviour during the day. He is afraid to go upstairs alone. He can't seem to tell me what the problem is. We are all exhausted and have shredded nerves.

This child needs reassurance at bedtime. His parents should stress that he is safe and that nothing can harm him. If his fears persist, however, it might be helpful for him to be referred to a psychologist for counselling.

Quite often night-time fears are learned. Fear of the dark can sometimes be learned by conditioning: if the child wakes from a frightening dream and his mother responds by entering his bedroom, switching on the light and offering comfort, she may unintentionally teach her child to associate light with feeling secure and darkness with distress. Night-time anxieties can be learned in other ways. The child may associate a particular stimulus, such as shadows in his bedroom, with fear, or he may be afraid to go to sleep because he has suffered nightmares. The bedroom can become associated with anxiety if it is used as a place to which the child is sent as a punishment. The child may be distressed by his parents arguing downstairs when he is in bed, and come to associate bedtime with anxiety.

What can I do about it?

Fears are a normal part of growing up and should not worry you unduly. Once your child has worked through his fears he will be able to return to his old sleep habits. The approach we use to deal with anxieties or night-time fears is quite different from the one we use for correcting settling and waking problems, in which you have to limit the attention you give to your child at night so that he can learn to be more independent. The aim here is to reassure your child so that he feels less anxious and more secure. This means you have to determine what is really stopping him from going to sleep before you decide which programme to use. Problems of settling and waking initially caused by anxieties or night-time fears can easily become habitual, so you need to be able to tell the difference between a genuinely frightened child and one who is just trying to postpone bedtime.

Most children have the occasional nightmare. Frequent night-time disturbance is usually caused not by nightmares but by sleep terrors or other partial wakings (see pages 187-195). If your child has a bad dream, go to him and offer comfort and reassurance. Let him know that he is safe and that you are nearby.

Like adults, children are often at their most insecure and fearful at night when they are tired and alone and it is dark. There are many things that can frighten a child at night. Fear of the dark, of being alone, or of bed-wetting may make it difficult for him to fall asleep. There is no reason why your child should sleep in total darkness if he does not like it. You can use a night light or a small gadget that plugs into an electric socket and lets out a glow. When your child wakes up in the night he can find his bearings in the room and check to see that everything is in its proper place. If the door is open he will not feel isolated. If you have more than one child, think about allowing the child to share a room with an older brother or sister. You need not worry that the fearful one will disturb the other child — they will work it out quickly if you don't interfere. The child will find the presence of a big brother or sister reassuring. The older child will not let the younger child disturb her sleep, and after a few nights of being ignored when he tries to talk the younger child will finally go to sleep himself.

If you don't want your children to share a bedroom or you don't have other children, you can usually deal with the problem by positive reinforcement or teaching the child relaxation techniques. Star charts can be used for reinforcement. A child receives a gold star on a special chart for spending progressively longer and longer periods without calling out for his parents (see Programme 6). Often a programme of gradual change, in which the parent initially sits with the child to offer support, then distances themself from the child's room, will be very successful (see Programme 8). You could try entering your child's bedroom when you are called without switching on the light. In this way security will begin to be associated with darkness. Alternatively, you could use a dimmer switch to reduce the amount of light in the bedroom gradually until your child learns to feel safe in the dark. As with other sleep problems, difficulties in settling or waking initially caused by night-time fears that have since resolved can quickly become habitual. The child learns to associate difficult bedtime behaviour with extra attention and cuddles. If your child's fears persist you could try either Programme 11 or Programme 12.

Programme 11

- ❖ Start a positive routine (see page 66). This should be a comforting time alone with one parent to help your child to unwind and prepare for sleep. Begin the routine at a set bedtime, follow the same sequence of events, and allow it to take 20-30 minutes each night.
- ❖ Help your child to become attached to a security object that he can keep in bed with him. This will often help him to feel less anxious at night.
- ❖ Try using a night light. The dark can trigger off any child's fears. You might also leave the bedroom door open so that your child feels closer to you and the rest of the family.
- ❖ If your child resists bedtimes or if he cries or calls out in fear, go in and reassure him. You can say something like 'John, you're quite safe here. We're here to make sure you stay safe. We'll make sure nothing hurts you, so you can relax and go to sleep'. Be reassuring but calm, adapting what you say to the child's particular fears. Make sure you communicate the idea of safety again and again.

- ❖ If your child wakes in the night and can't go back to sleep because of fears, do the same. Go in to his room and reassure him. Repeat the message about him being safe, that you are there to ensure he comes to no harm, and that he will be fine.
- ❖ Don't dismiss or laugh at your child's fears. These fears are very real to the child. He can't approach them rationally because of his developmental stage, and you must do your best not to undermine his confidence or make fun of his feelings. Listen to what your child is saying and reassure him.
- ❖ It is very important not to build up your child's fears. If he is afraid of robbers, for example, don't go round searching under the bed and in the cupboards looking for them. This will only fuel his fears. What is more, he may come to enjoy the prolonged ritual of you searching round the bedroom and the extra attention this brings.
- ❖ Don't get your child out of bed. The aim is to teach him to deal with and overcome his fears. If you allow him to sleep in your bed or come downstairs you are giving your child the message that his bedroom is not a safe place to be in. It is better for you to stay with him in his bedroom.
- ❖ If your child gets out of bed in the middle of the night and comes in to your room, take him back immediately. Reassure him, tuck him back in, stay for a few minutes if necessary, but don't let him get up. If your child is very frightened you can occasionally stay until he falls asleep, but don't do this too frequently or he will come to depend upon your presence to fall asleep.
- ❖ Try to build your child's confidence during the daytime. If he is old enough, you can talk about what was bothering him the night before to help him to overcome the fear.
- ❖ If your child's sleep disturbance continues despite these efforts, it may be that he has become used to the attention that being afraid brings. Be more firm for a few nights, while reassuring him that he is safe.
- ❖ Sometimes a child becomes particularly fearful and these simple measures don't work. If this happens, you can try Programme 12.
- ❖ Think of combining this programme with some relaxation training (Programme 14).

Programme 12

This programme combines relaxation skills, self-instruction, positive reinforcement, and coping skills training that is carried out through the use of story book characters. The story provides a model of two children who were afraid of going to sleep at night but have learned to overcome

*I am grateful to Roger Katz and Carol McMenamy of the University of the Pacific for allowing me to adapt the materials described in *Developmental and Behavioural Pediatrics,* 10, 3, 1989.

their fears through their own efforts. The programme is carried out in steps.*

- ❖ Decide on an appropriate bedtime. Don't vary it. At bedtime, instead of your usual bedtime story, carry out the following sequence.
- ❖ Ask your child to lie down in a comfortable position, close his eyes, and take deep breaths, using his diaphragm.
- ❖ Read the story below. It tells of two children who experience night-time fears and the methods they use to overcome this. While the story is being read, model each action the children in the story take, and ask your child to imitate it.
- ❖ Repeat each night before going to bed, encouraging your child to make 'brave' statements like the children in the story to distract themselves from fear arousing stimuli, eg 'I can look after myself at night', 'I am brave'.
- ❖ Provide reinforcement for your child for successfully performing the coping behaviours by using a star chart (see Programme 6). If he listens attentively to the story and successfully imitates the behaviours award him a red star for his star chart. Give a gold star in the morning if he has been able to cope with his fears on his own without calling for attention. After he has earned several stars in a row, you can exchange them for a small gift or toy that he chooses.
- ❖ Encourage your child to use these skills on his own whenever he is afraid of the dark.
- ❖ Be sure to monitor your child's progress by using the sleep diary. Note how long he takes to fall asleep and the frequency and intensity of crying, arguing, and getting out of bed. Each night make a note of how fearful he appears to be on a 5 point scale from 5 'very fearful' to 1 'not fearful at all'.
- ❖ Continue to read the story each night and to encourage your child to imitate the coping behaviours until his night-time fears start to decrease. You can then 'fade' the story, ie do not read it every night — read it perhaps every other night, then every three nights, then every five nights, until stopping completely. However, encourage your child to carry on performing the coping behaviours and carry on reinforcing 'brave' nights until the fears subside.

The Story of Emma and Tom

These children used to be afraid of going to sleep at night. They were afraid of the dark and of going to sleep on their own. They did not like feeling afraid. They wanted to feel cosy and safe at bedtime.

'Guess what? We're not afraid of the dark and of sleeping on our own any more! Now we feel cosy and safe and happy at night. Our Mum and Dad are very proud of us now too!'

'Would you like to learn how to feel cosy and safe at night too? Would you like to learn how to stop being afraid? Tom and I are going to show you how you can be brave like us. Are you ready?'

'First, we lie down and we let our bodies get really relaxed — no wriggling around now. Then to help us feel nice and relaxed we breathe in a special way. Your Mum or Dad will show you how to do this.'

'Now you do this too.'

'Next, we think about how nice it is to do our favourite things. We think about nice things like riding our bikes or eating ice cream during the day. What is your favourite thing?'

'Now you think about something nice too.'

'Then we say some special words out loud. We say that we are brave and that we don't have to be afraid when we are in bed at night. When we say that we are brave, we don't feel afraid any more!'

'Now you say the special words.'

'Now you can be brave like us!'

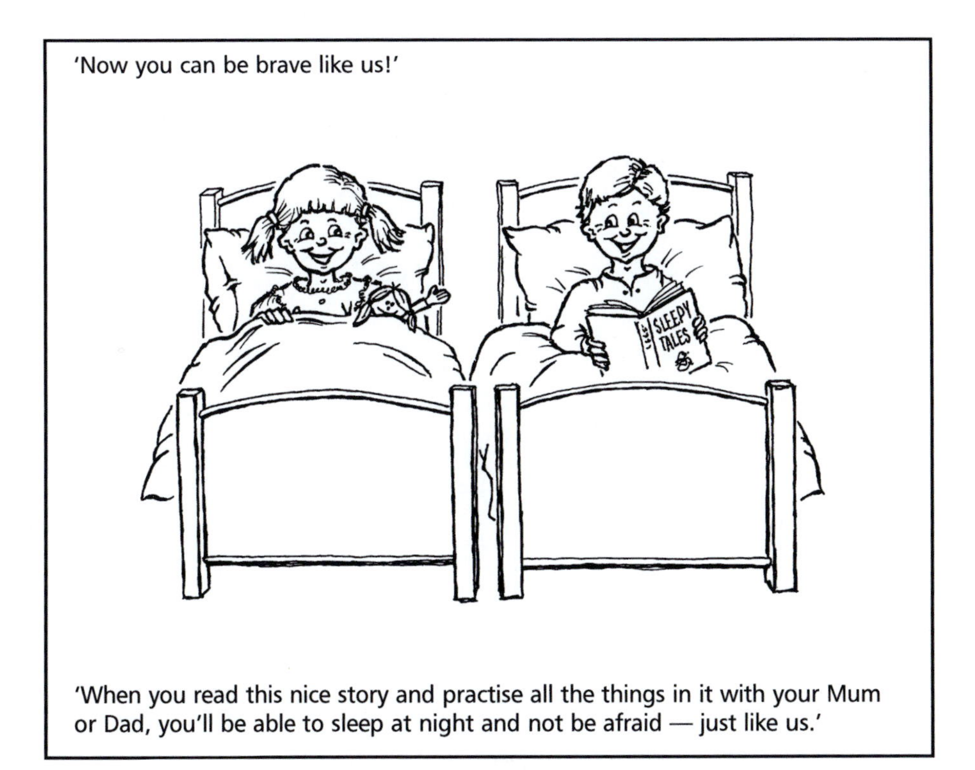

'When you read this nice story and practise all the things in it with your Mum or Dad, you'll be able to sleep at night and not be afraid — just like us.'

'When you stay in bed and act like a brave girl or boy, your Mum or Dad will give you a gold star to put on your chart. The more stars you have, the braver you are.'

WHEN YOU HAVE .... STARS OR MORE,

YOU WILL BE ABLE TO..

Difficulty Adjusting To Stress*

Difficulty adjusting to stress is a sleep disturbance related to a period of acute stress, anxiety, emotions, or environmental change. It sometimes develops before tests or examinations, or as a reaction to the first day of school or to family related problems. It is occasionally triggered by sleeping in an unfamiliar place. It can start when the child's security is suddenly threatened, for example by the arrival of a new baby or the death of a grandparent. Sometimes the reaction of children to a bereavement goes unnoticed because it is thought that they cannot understand such events. In particular, if a child has learning disabilities it is often thought that he is not aware of or sensitive to these events. However, all children, even those with learning disabilities, may suffer profound grief if a family member dies, even if they are unable to show how unhappy they are.

The disturbance caused by difficulty adjusting to stress is usually brief, with sleep quickly returning to normal levels, but occasionally, when parents have difficulties in handling the episode, it can become habitual, and then is more usefully treated as a limit setting problem.

What are the symptoms?

- ❖ Sleeplessness or occasionally daytime sleepiness
- ❖ Anxiety
- ❖ Bodily symptoms such as aches, pains, or headaches

The child may find it hard to fall asleep or may wake early, and may be anxious and tearful. The parent is usually able to identify the stressor, which may be watching a frightening TV film or family conflict or bereavement. Sometimes stressors include pleasant events such as the child's birthday or an eagerly awaited event such as a holiday.

How common is it?

The problem is thought to be very common in childhood. About one third of adults are thought to experience brief episodes each year. Children who are insecure or anxious are more vulnerable.

When does it start?

The problem may occur at any age.

How long does it last?

This problem is not usually long-lasting. It begins within about three months of the stressful event and usually disappears when the stressor is removed or the child adapts to the situation. If the stressor is acute the

*Adjustment sleep disorder.

episode is usually brief. If the stressor is long-lasting it may take the child some months to adjust. Occasionally the sleep disturbance becomes habitual and it is then more usefully treated as a limit setting problem.

Is my child suffering from difficulty adjusting to stress?

Your child is probably suffering from difficulty adjusting to stress if

❖ he begins to suffer from sleeplessness or excessive sleepiness after a stressful event.

❖ he is tired, or spends a long time in bed, or appears anxious, irritable, miserable, or depressed.

❖ he has aches, pains, sore eyes, or headaches.

❖ he finds it difficult to fall asleep, suffers from an increased number of awakenings, or wakes early.

❖ there is no evidence of a medical disorder that can account for the symptoms.

❖ the problem disappears when the stress is reduced or the child adapts.

Other problems to consider are **incorrect sleep associations** and **limit setting problems**.

What can I do about it?

The problem usually resolves when the child adapts. Occasionally it persists and can be dealt with in much the same way as night-time fears. It is important to determine the origin of the problem so that understanding and support may be given. Try to assess how frightened your child really is. If there are no signs of real panic, be firm, say goodnight, and leave. If the fears are extreme and your child is truly panicky and afraid to be left alone to sleep, you can use Programme 13 to get him gradually used to settling to sleep alone. You can also use Programme 14 to help him to relax at bedtime.

Programme 13

This is a graded steps programme which is suitable for the very anxi child or the child who has been upset by bereavement, illness, or famil stress.

Step 1 Decide on an appropriate bedtime. Once you have decided on a reasonable time, don't vary it. A consistent bedtime will help your child learn to anticipate bedtime and set up the right sleep associations.

Step 2 Start a regular, relaxing bedtime routine, such as giving a bath, putting the child into pyjamas, playing music or reading a story. The routine will help him to relax and unwind, ready to go to sleep. Begin the routine at a set time each night and allow about half an hour per night. Be calm and matter-of-fact. If you are anxious your child will pick this up and get anxious too.

Step 3 Once the routine is complete, say goodnight. Your goal is now to help your child to relax and fall asleep so that you can distance yourself gradually from his room in a series of steps which will take a few days to complete. Be supportive and reassuring but firm. Your child should know that you are still near to take care of him.

Step 4 On the first night of the programme, after the bedtime routine, sit rather than lying down on the child's bed until he goes to sleep. Resist attempts by the child to persuade you to lie down on the bed.

Repeat this on the subsequent 2-3 nights, until the child tolerates it without fuss. Allow him to go to sleep before you leave the room. When he has accepted this step, proceed to Step 5. Do not rush the programme. The aim is gradually to 'desensitise' your child to a previously frightening situation — having to go to sleep alone. His fears must be gradually allowed to fade away and become extinguished since they are not being reinforced/rewarded by your attention.

Step 5 Instead of sitting on the bed, place a chair beside it. Sit on the chair, perhaps touching the child. Do this for 2-3 nights, until he tolerates this without fuss. Allow him to fall asleep before you leave the room. Then proceed to Step 6.

Step 6 Sit by the bed, not touching the child. Do this for 2-3 nights, allowing him to fall asleep before you leave the room. When he tolerates this without fuss proceed to Step 7.

Step 7 Sit at gradually increasing distances from the child's bed. You must decide how many steps to take. Each time you move the chair, leave it in the same spot for 2-3 nights. As each stage is established you can move your chair gradually towards the door.

lly, place the chair outside the bedroom door or sit on the t there until the child falls asleep. Do this for 2-3 nights.

child tolerates this stage without fuss, you can take the nd enjoy your evening.

you have said goodnight, do not talk to or play with your child. Try not to establish eye contact with him or to smile at him. You are not there to keep him company or talk to him. You are simply there to reassure him and to ensure that he comes to no harm while falling asleep.

Give lavish praise the next morning each time the child settles easily. You can also try other rewards. Do this in a consistent way (see pages 62-64).

Think of combining this programme with relaxation training (see Programme 14).

Fill in a sleep diary every night to monitor your child's progress.

Programme 14[*]

This programme teaches the child to relax ready for bed. It is suitable for the child who is very anxious at night or is afraid to go to bed. You can do this exercise together with your child for a few minutes each night before bedtime. The relaxation exercises involve consistently tensing and relaxing muscles in an orderly sequence until all the main muscle groups in the body are relaxed. They are based on the idea that muscle tension is related to anxiety and your child will begin to feel less anxious as she relaxes her muscles. Use this script:

Hands and arms

Make a fist with your left hand. Squeeze it hard. Feel the tightness in your hand and arm as you squeeze. Now let your hand go and relax. See how much better your hand and arm feel when they are relaxed. Once again, make a fist with your left hand and squeeze hard. Good. Now relax and let your hand go. (Repeat the process for the right hand and arm.)

Arms and shoulders

Stretch your arms out in front of you. Raise them high up over your head. Way back. Feel the pull in your shoulders. Stretch higher. Now just let your arms drop back to your side. Okay, let's stretch again. Stretch your arms out in front of you. Raise them over your head. Pull them back, way back. Pull hard. Now let them drop quickly. Good. Notice how your shoulders feel more relaxed. This time let's have a great big stretch. Try to touch the ceiling. Stretch your arms way out in front of you. Raise them

*This programme is adapted from
Ollendick T H and Cerny J A, *Clinical Behaviour Therapy with Children*. New York: Plenum, 1982.

way up high over your head. Push them way, way back. Notice the tension and pull in your arms and shoulders. Hold tight, now. Great. Let them drop very quickly and feel how good it is to be relaxed. It feels nice and warm and lazy.

Shoulders and neck

Try to pull your shoulders up to your ears and push your head down into your shoulders. Hold in tight. Okay, now relax and feel the warmth. Again, pull your shoulders up to your ears and push your head down into your shoulders. Do it tightly. Okay, you can relax now. Bring your head out and let your shoulders relax. Notice how much better it feels to be relaxed than to be all tight. One more time now. Push your head down and your shoulders way up to your ears. Hold it. Feel the tension in your neck and shoulders. Okay. You can relax now and feel comfortable. You feel good.

Jaw

Put your teeth together really hard. Let your neck muscles help you. Now relax. Just let your jaw hang loose. Notice how good it feels just to let your jaw drop. Okay, bite down again hard. That's good. Now relax again. Just let your jaw drop. It feels so good just to let go. Okay, one more time. Bite down. Hard as you can. Harder. Oh, you're really working hard. Good. Now relax. Try to relax your whole body. Let yourself go as loose as you can.

Face and nose

Wrinkle up your nose. Make as many wrinkles in your nose as you can. Scrunch your nose up really hard. Good. Now you can relax your nose. Now wrinkle up your nose again. Wrinkle it up hard. Hold it just as tight as you can. Okay. You can relax your face. Notice when you scrunch up your nose that your cheeks and your mouth and your forehead all help you and they get tight too. So when you relax your nose, your whole face relaxes too, and that feels good. Now make lots of wrinkles on your forehead. Hold it tight, now. Okay, you can let go. Now you can just relax. Let your face go smooth. No wrinkles anywhere. Your face feels nice and smooth and relaxed.

Stomach

Now tighten up your stomach muscles really tight. Make your stomach really hard. Don't move. Hold it. You can relax now. Let your stomach go soft. Let it be as relaxed as you can. That feels so much better. Okay, again. Tighten your stomach really hard. Good. You can relax now. Settle down, get comfortable, and relax. Notice the difference between a tight stomach and a relaxed one. That's how we want it to feel. Nice and loose and relaxed. Okay, once more. Tighten up. Tighten hard. Good. Now you can relax completely. You can feel nice and relaxed.

This time, try to pull your stomach in. Try to squeeze it against your backbone. Try to be as thin as you can. Now relax. You don't have to be thin now. Just relax and feel your stomach being warm and loose. Okay, squeeze in your stomach again. Make it touch your backbone. Get it really small and tight. Get as thin as you can. Hold tight now. You can relax now. Settle back and let your stomach come back out where it belongs. You can really feel good now. You've done really well.

Legs and feet

Push your toes down on the floor really hard. You'll probably need your legs to help you push. Push down, spread your toes apart. Now relax your feet. Let your toes go loose and feel how nice that is. It feels good to be relaxed. Okay. Now push your toes down. Let your leg muscles help you push your feet down. Push your feet. Hard. Relax your feet, relax your legs, relax your toes. It feels so good to be relaxed. No tension anywhere. You feel warm and tingly.

Conclusion

Close your eyes. Stay as relaxed as you can. Let your whole body go limp and feel all your muscles relaxed. In a few minutes I'll ask you to open your eyes. Shake your arms. Now shake your legs. Move your head around. Slowly open your eyes. Very good. You've done a good job. Now you're relaxed it will be easy for you to go to sleep.

Night Time Feeding Problems*

Night-time feeding problems result in recurrent wakings after which the child is unable to go back to sleep without eating or drinking. Once the child has been given a bottle or drink return to sleep is speedy.

This problem is found mainly in infancy and early childhood. The child consumes large amounts of liquid by breast feeding or bottle feeding when she wakes in the night. The problem usually begins when the child is nursed to sleep with either breast or bottle, then fed repeatedly during the night. Such children consume between 12 and 32 ounces of fluid during the night and may wake from three to eight times per night. In the morning their nappies are usually soaked.

After about six months of age babies no longer need to be fed at night. A few continue to wake and cry to be fed. Waking to eat/drink may be caused by three factors: (1) the child may associate feeding with going to sleep and returning to sleep; (2) she may have 'learned' to be hungry during the night; (3) having a full bladder may cause her to wake.

Frequent nightly feedings may disrupt the circadian rhythm and affect the child's sleep-wake cycle. The child remains on a pattern more typical of early infancy, with broken sleep and frequent feeding throughout the night. Learning to sleep through the night, which usually takes place at three to six months, is disrupted.

What are the symptoms?

- Difficulty staying asleep
- Frequent, repeated wakings to eat or drink
- Very large amounts of fluid are consumed throughout the night
- Soaked nappies in the morning

How common is it?

It has been estimated that 5% of children between six months and three years experience this problem. Because not all children offered breast or bottle at bedtime and night-time wakings fail to learn to sleep through the night, temperamental factors are suspected. The irritable or fussy child is vulnerable. The problem is more likely to occur if the parents believe that feeding should be continued until the child no longer demands it. Sometimes it is hard for parents to distinguish true need from habit, and because the child seems hungry at night, they assume she should be fed. Sometimes the mother enjoys nursing her child and continues for this reason. The child who is always offered a bottle or drink whenever there is

*Nocturnal eating/drinking syndrome.

any upset during the day may be slow to learn to deal with night-time wakings in any other way.

When does it start?

The problem may be present from early infancy but should not be a cause for concern until after six months of age when sleeping through the night is expected.

How long does it last?

This depends on the individual child. Some children stop waking without feedings ever being withheld, while others continue until their parents set limits. These children may continue waking until they are weaned completely at 3-4 years. Sometimes a child who has been weaned will continue to take milk or juice during the night from a cup. In this case, waking will persist.

Does my child have a night-time feeding problem?

Your child probably has a night-time feeding problem if

- ❖ she has difficulty staying asleep.
- ❖ she wakes frequently and recurrently to eat or drink.
- ❖ she falls asleep normally after eating or drinking.
- ❖ there is no other sleep problem producing difficulty in maintaining sleep.

Other problems to consider are **incorrect sleep associations** and **limit setting problems**. If incorrect sleep associations are the problem, children wake less often — perhaps only once or twice per night, and return to sleep rapidly after only a brief period at the breast or bottle. If the child wakes more frequently and drinks very large amounts of fluid (4-8 ounces each feed), then it is likely that it is a night-time feeding problem. As a general rule, if a child over six months is breast or bottle fed more than twice a night and nursing times are longer than 2-3 minutes, excessive night-time feeding is the problem. If the child has learned to feed during the night, frequent wakings will occur.

What can I do about it?

Programme 15 will help you to phase out night-time feeding either by gradually reducing the amount of each feed or by diluting the juice or milk you give your child. As the feeds become less and less rewarding your child will stop waking in the night.

Programme 15

This problem is very easy to solve. The aim is gradually to stop feeding your child at night. Children under six months of age still need feeding at night, so do not use this programme if your baby is less than six months old.

- For the bottle fed baby, the volume of fluid in each bottle given at night should be reduced over the course of two weeks. Your child will often stop waking to be fed when only 1-2 ounces are provided. Alternatively, the formula can be gradually diluted with water until your child is weaned from the bottle. If she is a juice guzzler, gradual dilution of orange juice with water works well. With the breast fed baby it is a little more difficult. If you are breast feeding you may have to express your milk manually and let the baby's father give the feed. Your milk should be gradually diluted with water and the child weaned from the bottle in the same way as the bottle fed baby.

- You want to accomplish two things. The first is to cut out night-time feedings to avoid disturbing your sleep and to help your child to learn to be hungry at the right times of the day. The second is to teach your child new sleep associations so that she can fall asleep alone without your presence or her bottle. You may choose to decrease the speed with which you respond to your child's crying when she wakes at the same time as reducing the feeding. Programme 7 will help you to do this. If you feel that it is too much to do at the same time, go in to comfort your child as soon as she wakes at the times when she would previously have been fed. Once the feedings stop you can then work on your child's sleep associations. The chart on page 134 will help you to do this.

- If your child cries when feeding is over, or if she wakes and cries less than three hours after the last feed, do not feed her again. She does not really need feeding. Remember that you are teaching her to feel hungry only during the daytime.

- The charts below give examples of both methods of treatment. Don't forget to monitor your child's progress by writing down how much fluid you have offered.

Treating Night-time Feeding Problems By Reducing Feeds

	Amount in each bottle	Minutes breast feeding
Before treatment	8 oz	8
Day 1	7½ oz	7½
Day 2	7 oz	7
Day 3	6½ oz	6½
Day 4	6 oz	6
Day 5	5½ oz	5½
Day 6	5 oz	5
Day 7	4½ oz	4½
Day 8	4 oz	4
Day 9	3½ oz	3½
Day 10	3 oz	3
Day 11	2½ oz	2½
Day 12	2 oz	2
Day 13	1½ oz	1½
Day 14	1 oz	1
Day 15	½ oz	½
Day 16	0	0

These are general guidelines. You can change them to fit your own requirements. If your child drinks less than eight ounces in the bottle, start with half an ounce less than she usually takes and reduce by half an ounce every day. If you are breast feeding, begin by feeding for one or two minutes less than usual and continue decreasing by about half a minute from that point. Using this method you can decrease every day or every other day. You can also try increasing the time between feedings by half an hour each time.

Treating Night-time Feeding Problems By Diluting Milk/Juice

	Amount of juice/milk in bottle
Before treatment	8 oz juice/milk
Day 1	7½ oz juice/ milk + ½ oz water
Day 2	7 + 1 oz
Day 3	6½ + 1½ oz
Day 4	6 + 2 oz
Day 5	5½ + 2½ oz
Day 6	5 + 3 oz
Day 7	4½ + 3½ oz
Day 8	4 + 4 oz
Day 9	3½ + 4½ oz
Day 10	3 + 5 oz
Day 11	2½ + 5½ oz
Day 12	2 + 6 oz
Day 13	1½ + 6½ oz
Day 14	1 + 7 oz
Day 15	½ + 7½ oz

The child will usually stop waking to feed long before the bottle contains all water. It isn't worth her while to wake up when the feeds are not rewarding.

FOOD ALLERGIES*

Severe disturbance in sleep during early infancy is sometimes brought about by cow's milk allergy. It is often difficult to tell the difference between colic and cow's milk allergy because both begin at similar ages and have similar symptoms of sleeplessness, fussiness, crying, and short sleep periods. Children with cow's milk allergy find it hard to fall asleep and wake up five or more times a night. Their total sleep time is often as little as 4½ hours every night. They also cry frequently during the day and are often described by their parents as 'fussy' children. The symptoms are resolved when cow's milk based formula is discontinued. For example, one study investigated 17 children for whose sleep problems no other cause could be found. When they were taken off all milk products, sleep became normal for 15 of them, with night waking disappearing. When milk was reintroduced sleeplessness reappeared in 14 children. Occasionally other food allergies cause problems with sleeping. The foods that are most commonly associated with food allergy are corn, wheat, chocolate, nuts, egg whites, yeast, and red and yellow dyes. If you remove the suspected food from your child's diet, normal sleep will often resume immediately.

What are the symptoms?

- Difficulty going to sleep
- Frequent wakings and crying
- Short total sleep time (often as little as 4½ hours)
- Fussiness during the day
- There may be physical symptoms such as skin irritations, breathing difficulties, or tummy upsets

How common are they?

The problem is common in childhood. A family history of food allergy may increase the risk.

When do they start?

Symptoms can occur from birth or from the introduction of cow's milk to the diet.

How long do they last?

Food allergies usually resolve spontaneously by the age of 2-4 years.

*Food allergy insomnia.

Does my child have a food allergy?

Your child may have a food allergy if

- ❖ you find that he has difficulty in going to sleep or wakes very frequently.
- ❖ the total sleep time is short.
- ❖ there is daytime tiredness.
- ❖ he gets very agitated when crying, waving his arms and legs in the air.
- ❖ removing the suspected food from the diet restores normal sleep within four weeks.
- ❖ there may be physical symptoms such as daytime tiredness, skin irritations, and tummy upsets.
- ❖ there is no evidence of a medical disorder that can account for the symptoms.

Another problem to consider is **colic**. It is often difficult to tell food allergies from colic since both begin at similar ages and are associated with fussiness, intermittent crying, and short sleep periods.

What can I do about it?

Programme 16 gives advice on how to deal with food allergies.

Programme 16

A number of food allergies can disturb a child's sleep. You can check this by removing the suspected foods one by one from your child's diet and seeing if the problem resolves. Here we give the example of cow's milk allergy.

- ❖ If you think your child's sleep problem may be caused by cow's milk allergy, you can try replacing cow's milk with dried milk formula. Within 2-4 weeks of the dietary change, sleep patterns will generally improve. Daytime symptoms will decrease or disappear completely and total sleep time will increase to the normal level for the child's age. Night wakings should decrease. If you reintroduce cow's milk the symptoms will return.
- ❖ Sometimes children who have had a food allergy develop abnormal habits around sleep because of the extra attention that parents have had to offer the crying child. If the child's daytime sleeps and symptoms improve, try Programme 7 or 8 to get your child used to falling asleep on his own again.

Irregular Sleep-Wake Patterns

If a regular routine around going to sleep and waking is not maintained, the child my develop an irregular sleep-wake pattern. The child falls asleep earlier than usual one night, then later than usual the next, wakes up during the night at strange hours and takes short sleeps during the daytime. Some families live somewhat chaotic lives, in which meal times are irregular and the whole of the child's daytime schedule is unpredictable. Bedtimes vary wildly and sometimes the child is left to fall asleep downstairs, then carried up to bed. If the child's sleep is not structured, the whole circadian rhythm may become disrupted.

As we have noted, our 'biological clock' is reset daily in order for our circadian rhythms to function properly. For this to work successfully, time cues such as light, dark, bedtime, wake time, meals, and patterns of daily activity need to be consistent and regular. When regular signals are not present, the child may sleep irregularly at night. Her body no longer knows when to sleep and when to wake.

What are the symptoms?

❖ Difficulty in falling asleep and staying asleep at night

❖ Excessive sleepiness during the daytime

❖ Frequent daytime sleeps

❖ Irregular pattern of at least three sleep periods during the 24-hour day

You may find the child is unable to fall asleep at the desired bedtime or to remain asleep for an adequate time. She may wake in the night several times. Parents often feel that their child never sleeps. There may be bedtime battles, prolonged night wakings, or daytime sleepiness. The child may seem tired and lacking in energy. She may find it hard to concentrate, school work may suffer, and the child may exhibit behavioural problems. Recording her sleep-wake times in a sleep diary will show up this irregular pattern.

How common is it?

The problem is rare in the general population but thought to be more common among children with severe neurological problems, visual impairments or chronic illness. However, it has been reported in non-handicapped children whose daily schedules have become disrupted.

When does it start?

The problem can start early in the child's life.

How long does it last?

The problem tends to be long-lasting.

Does my child have an irregular sleep-wake pattern?

Your child probably has an irregular sleep-wake pattern if

- ❖ she suffers from either sleeplessness or excessive sleepiness.
- ❖ there is an irregular sleep pattern with sleep broken into at least three blocks during the 24-hour period. Bedtimes and wake times occur at varying times.
- ❖ total sleep time per 24-hour period is normal for the child's age.
- ❖ the pattern has been present for at least three months.
- ❖ there is no underlying medical condition that can account for the symptoms.

Other problems to consider are early sleep phase, late sleep phase, and limit setting problems.

What can I do about it?

It is important for children's sleep that a regular bedtime is decided upon and kept to, and that the child is woken at the same time each morning. Programme 17 will help you to establish a more regular routine for your child.

Programme 17

Use this programme if your child's sleeping and waking patterns have become completely disorganised and the child is waking at different times in the day and night.

Step 1 Use the sleep log on page 165 to chart your child's sleeping and waking patterns. If an irregular sleep-wake pattern is the problem the chart will show no regular pattern. Wake times and sleep times will be erratic and disorganised.

Step 2 Set up a daily schedule for your child so that bedtimes, wake times, daytime sleeps and mealtimes are regular and consistent.

Step 3 Decide on a bedtime routine (see page 66). Keep to the routine, carrying out the same activities in the same order for about 20-30 minutes each evening when your child goes to bed. This will provide your child with a clear cue that bedtime is coming.

Step 4 Put your child to bed and wake her up at the set time each evening and morning — even at weekends.

If your child is young enough to need a daytime sleep, keep this at a regular time. Wake your child when the daytime sleep period is over. Do not allow her to sleep at other times.

The purpose of all these regular activities is to help your child to reset her biological clock and establish a regular sleep-wake pattern.

Make sure your child falls asleep in her own bed, alone. You can sit with her and slowly distance yourself from the room in stages.

Make sure your child stays in bed once you have said goodnight. You can use Programme 2 or 4 to achieve this. Be firm but supportive.

If your child wakes during the night you can go in to reassure her, but do not play games, cuddle her or read stories. This will only reinforce the wakings.

It should take about 10-14 days for your child's sleep pattern to become more regular.

You can use positive reinforcement with this programme (see pages 62-64). When your child has achieved a regular night's sleep, give her extra praise, hugs, and attention when you go in to her in the morning, or you could use a star chart (see Programme 6).

Keep a diary of your child's sleep patterns for several weeks to make sure that the pattern is properly established.

Once your child's sleep patterns are re-established you can be more flexible, but remember that if her sleep patterns have been disrupted in the past they may easily become irregular again unless you are careful. Consistent daily routines are very important for the child who is vulnerable to this problem. Sometimes the child's daily routines lack structure because of family problems. These may be illness, bereavement, marital unhappiness, or divorce in the family, which make it difficult for parents to maintain a normal routine for their children. It is important that parents with these problems seek appropriate help.

Completing a Sleep Log

1. Draw an arrow down (▼) when your child gets into bed.
2. Shade in the boxes (■) when your child is sleeping.
3. Leave the boxes blank when your child is awake, even if in bed.
4. Draw an arrow up (▲) when your child gets out of bed.
5. NOTE: Each line of boxes represents parts of TWO days!

SLEEP LOG

Day	6	7	8	9	10	11	Midnight ↓	1	2	3	4	5	6	7	8	9	10	11	Noon ↓	1	2	3	4	5	Comments

Late Sleep Phase*

If your child's natural sleep period takes place later in the 24-hour day than is appropriate for his age and development, he may have a late sleep phase. The child sleeps well, but at the wrong times. Such children are not ready for sleep until late in the evening and would not wake until late in the morning if allowed. Parents think that the child should be ready to go to bed long before he is physiologically ready for sleep. This results in settling problems and bedtime struggles, and difficulty in waking the child in the morning. The child appears tired during the morning and may fall asleep at school. Night wakings are not usually a problem. Once asleep the child stays asleep.

Although there are various reasons why a child develops a late sleep phase the most common is a lack of regularly enforced bedtimes and wake times. Parents who allow their children to sleep late in the mornings often do so because they like to sleep late themselves.

"Are you joining us for lunch?"

*Delayed sleep phase syndrome.

What are the symptoms?

- ❖ Inability to fall asleep within two hours or the desired sleep time, or inability to wake up at the right time
- ❖ Excessive daytime sleepiness
- ❖ Bedtime battles

Because the parents' expectations for bedtime may be earlier than the time the child is physiologically ready for sleep, the usual complaint is of bedtime battles. The child will have difficulty in falling asleep at the expected bedtime. If bedtime is delayed, there are no battles. Parents also report difficulties in waking the child in the morning. The child appears very sleepy and unable to wake properly. His behaviour and activities in the morning are sluggish, and his school performance may be poor. The child may fall asleep at school. In contrast, he will appear alert and energetic late in the evening. At weekends, when bedtimes are later, struggles are fewer and children may 'catch up' on sleep they have missed because they have been woken in the morning to go to school. Occasional late bedtimes followed by recovery morning sleep is enough to shift some children's sleep phase. Holidays on which the child is allowed to stay up or illness may trigger this problem.

How common is it?

Late sleep phase is common during childhood and adolescence. Children with neurological problems seem particularly vulnerable.

When does it start?

The problem most commonly begins in adolescence, though childhood cases, particularly among children with neurological disorder or learning disabilities, have been reported.

How long does it last?

The problem can last for many years.

Does my child have a late sleep phase?

Your child probably has a late sleep phase if

- ❖ he is unable to fall asleep at the desired clock time or wake up spontaneously at the desired time of waking.
- ❖ he suffers from excessive sleepiness during the day.
- ❖ the sleep phase has shifted, so that it occurs at the wrong time.
- ❖ symptoms are present for at least one month.
- ❖ once asleep the child stays asleep and rarely wakes.

- a sleep diary shows a delay in the timing of habitual sleep for at least two weeks.

Other problems to consider are **limit setting problems, irregular sleep-wake pattern**, and **poor sleep hygiene**. Late sleep phase differs from limit setting problems in the following ways:

1. Even when limits are firmly set and the child is put to bed at a set time he takes a long time to fall asleep. The time of going to sleep is fairly independent of bedtime.
2. Night-time sleep is usually continuous once the child has gone to sleep.
3. If the child is allowed to wake naturally he will usually sleep on into the morning.

What can I do about it?

Late sleep phase can be corrected quite easily by following Programme 18, 19, or 20. Programme 18 is suitable for a child who has a shift or three hours or less and does not have to get up at a set time to go to school. If your child has to get up at a set time on weekdays because of school, use Programme 19. Programme 20 is for teenagers with a shift of several hours.

Programme 18

This programme is a graded steps programme which will regularise the sleep schedule of the young child whose natural sleep period has shifted to later than you would like. It is suitable for a child who has a shift of three hours or less. The programme involves starting with a schedule that fits your child's present pattern of falling asleep and waking, and then gradually advancing the sleep phase by making bedtimes and wake times a little earlier every day. You can therefore only carry out this programme with children under school age, or during the holidays. If your child has to get up at an early hour on weekdays because of school, use Programme 19.

Step 1 For the first 2 days the child should be allowed to fall asleep and wake at the times he has become used to. The time of falling asleep may be very late in the evening, and the child may not wake until mid morning. Usually your child will fall asleep easily at this time. Bedtime struggles will disappear, and the child will wake without difficulty in the morning, although it may be very late.

Step 2 From Day 3, begin to wake and get the child up approximately 15-30 minutes earlier each day, keeping the bedtime constant at the sleep time established on the previous 2 days (see Figure 1). Do this for 3 days without changing the bedtime.

Step 3 When the waking time has been advanced by 45-60 minutes (Day 5 or 6), you should begin to bring the bedtime forward slowly by 15-30 minutes per night.

Step 4 When the desired morning wake time is reached, it should be firmly and consistently fixed (even in holidays and at weekends).

Step 5 Bedtime should be advanced slowly until the desired time is reached, and then firmly fixed. The total sleep time should then be similar to that shown for a child of similar age on page 16. Figure 2 gives an example.

For a short period during the course of this programme your child will be somewhat deprived of sleep, since you are getting him up earlier each day but his time of going to sleep is the same. He will probably be irritable and tired on these days but should not be allowed to take naps since this would interfere with the treatment. If the sleep phase has shifted by more than four hours, use Programme 20. It is very rare for children and young adolescents to have delays of more than four hours.

Be sure to follow the schedule carefully and record your child's sleep patterns in the sleep log on page 165 so that you can monitor his progress.

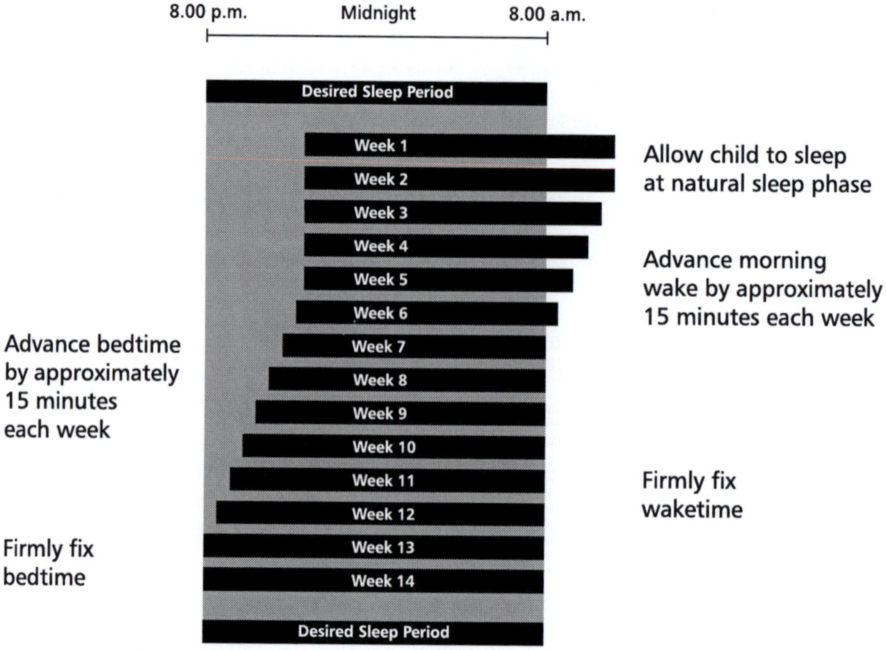

Figure 1

	Bedtime	Waking
Sleep phase before starting programme	**10.00 pm**	**10.00 am**
Week 1	10.00 pm	10.00 am
Week 2	10.00 pm	10.00 am
Week 3	10.00 pm	9.45 am
Week 4	10.00 pm	9.30 am
Week 5	10.00 pm	9.15 am
Week 6	10.00 pm	9.00 am
Week 7	9.45 pm	8.45 am
Week 8	9.30 pm	8.30 am
Week 9	9.15 pm	8.15 am
Week 10	9.00 pm	8.00 am
Week 11	8.45 pm	8.00 am
Week 12	8.30 pm	8.00 am
Week 13	8.15 pm	8.00 am
Week 14	8.00 pm	8.00 am
Sleep phase after finishing programme	**8.00 pm**	**8.00 am**

Figure 2

Programme 19

How to Solve Late Sleep Phase: Programme for Children at School

If your child has to get up at an early hour on weekdays because of school, you have less choice and will have to work with the bedtime schedule. You can't let her sleep late and begin to wake her progressively earlier because she needs to get up for school. However, you should still start with a late bedtime. Here is what you do.

Step 1 Allow your child to go to sleep at the late bedtime she has become used to for 2-3 weeks, but wake her up at the same time each day. Bedtime might be as late as 11pm for these weeks. This will leave her rather tired each day, but as long as you don't allow her to take daytime sleeps it will be easier for her to fall asleep at an earlier hour when you start to advance her bedtime. When your child is allowed to go to bed and to sleep at her 'natural' time, bedtime battles will disappear, bedtimes will be peaceful, and you will be able to start a relaxing routine with your child.

Step 2 From the beginning of the third week onwards, put your child to bed 15 minutes earlier each week (see Figures 3 and 4). The gradual changes will prevent her from lying awake for long periods. The morning wake times should be kept consistent.

Step 3 Keep making bedtimes 15 minutes earlier each week until the desired bedtime is reached. You will find that bedtime is now a more enjoyable experience for both you and your child. The programme means that you will have to get up early at weekends for a while, but it will be worth the inconvenience. When the problem is solved your child will begin waking on her own at the right time in the morning. This will show you that the sleep phase has repositioned itself to an appropriate time in the 24 hour day. You can now be more relaxed about getting up at weekends.

Fill in a daily sleep log (see page 165) to monitor your child's progress.

Don't forget the bedtime routine.

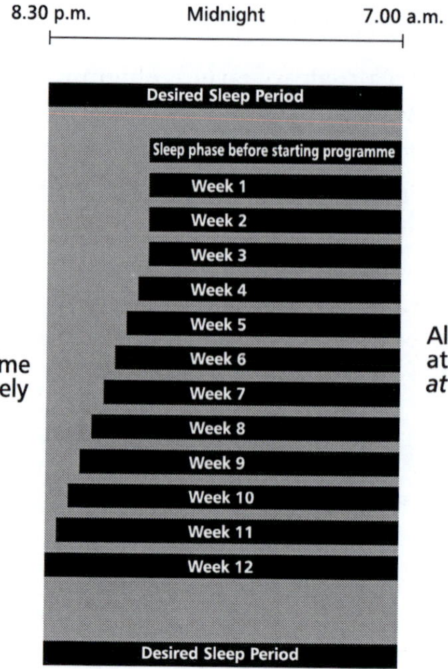

Figure 3

	Bedtime	**Waking**
Sleep phase before starting programme	**11.00 pm**	**7.00 am**
Week 1	11.00 pm	7.00 am
Week 2	11.00 pm	7.00 am
Week 3	10.45 pm	7.00 am
Week 4	10.30 pm	7.00 am
Week 5	10.15 pm	7.00 am
Week 6	10.00 pm	7.00 am
Week 7	9.45 pm	7.00 am
Week 8	9.30 pm	7.00 am
Week 9	9.15 pm	7.00 am
Week 10	9.00 pm	7.00 am
Week 11	8.45 pm	7.00 am
Week 12	8.30 pm	7.00 am
Sleep phase after finishing programme	**8.30 pm**	**7.00 am**

Figure 4

Programme 20

How to Solve Late Sleep Phase in Teenagers

Older teenagers quite often experience problems with a delayed sleep phase. Late sleep phase problems are more difficult to solve in teenagers because they typically go to bed several hours after an appropriate bedtime. In order to regularise such a schedule you will need to attempt a controlled 'around the clock' phase delay. You should try this during a holiday when your teenager has no social responsibilities, because during one period your teenager will be asleep all day and awake all night. The easiest way to start is for your teenager to start going to bed later each night until he has gone round the clock to the appropriate time.

- Delay bedtime by two hours each night (see Figure 5). Allow the teenager to sleep as long as he wants.
- Continue the 2 hour delays until the desired sleep phase is reached, eg 11pm to 7am. When this occurs firmly fix the morning wake time and keep it consistent on schooldays, weekends, and holidays. Bedtimes should also be firmly fixed.
- Exposing the teenager to a brightly lit environment for several hours after waking may help to advance the sleep phase to the desired times.
- Fill in a daily sleep log (see p.165) to monitor your child's progress.

	Bedtime	**Waking**
Sleep phase before starting programme	**2.30 am**	**10.30 am**
Monday	4.30 am	12.30 pm
Tuesday	6.30 am	2.30 pm
Wednesday	8.30 am	4.30 pm
Thursday	10.30 am	6.30 pm
Friday	12.30 pm	8.30 pm
Saturday	2.30 pm	10.30 pm
Sunday	4.30 pm	12.30 am
Monday	6.30 pm	2.30 am
Tuesday	8.30 pm	4.30 am
Wednesday	10.30 pm	6.30 am
Sleep phase after finishing programme	**11.00 pm**	**7.00 am**

Figure 5

Early Sleep Phase*

Early sleep phase is an uncommon problem that results in symptoms of tiredness and sleepiness early in the evening and early morning waking. It occurs most often in very young children and usually disappears when evening activities help to train the child to achieve a normal sleep phase.

What are the symptoms?

- Inability to stay awake until the desired bedtime
- Early morning waking (up to two hours earlier than desired)

The problem lies in early morning waking. You may find that your child is awake, alert, and wanting to get up in the very early morning and bounces into your bedroom at half past four or five in the morning demanding games and attention, or wakes you early by noisy crying. However, the child is ready to go to bed and to settle very early and easily in the evening. Total sleep time is normal, but sleep occurs at an inappropriate time. If your child is forced to remain awake until later in the evening she will be irritable and difficult to manage. If her daily schedule is examined you may find that the entire day is advanced. Meal times and nap times are earlier than the norms for her age.

How common is it?

The problem is rare and is usually found only in very young children.

When does it start?

Occurs sometimes in children a few months old and resolves in early childhood.

How long does it last?

The problem usually resolves as the child gets older.

Has my child developed an early sleep phase?

Your child may have developed an early sleep phase if

- she is consistently unable to stay awake until the desired/appropriate bedtime or she wakes inappropriately early in the morning.
- the child's sleep phase has shifted to an earlier time in the 24-hour day.
- symptoms are present for at least three months.
- if the child is allowed to sleep when she wants to, she consistently falls asleep earlier than desired and wakes very early in the morning.

*Advanced sleep phase syndrome.

Other problems to consider are **limit setting problems** and **insufficient sleep**.

What can I do about it?

Solving the problem is straightforward and if you follow Programme 21 the problem should get better quite quickly. Delaying the sleep phase is easier than advancing the sleep phase since there is a tendency for our natural pacemakers to shift back by about one hour for every 24 hour period if not firmly fixed. When the desired bedtime and morning waking time have been achieved they should be carefully adhered to every night. It is important to be both persistent and consistent. Keeping a sleep log will help to monitor progress.

Programme 21

- ❖ Decide on an appropriate bedtime. Set up a bedtime routine. Begin by delaying your child's bedtime for 15 minutes each day (see Figures 6 and 7). Allow the morning waking to occur spontaneously, when the child is ready to wake.
- ❖ As the desired bedtime is reached, morning wake times will gradually become later.
- ❖ When the desired bedtime is reached, firmly fix both bedtime and wake time (including weekends and holidays).
- ❖ Delay meal times and daytime sleeps day by day in the same way to fit the new schedule.
- ❖ You can relax the weekend schedule after a few weeks when your child's sleep phase has repositioned itself to a better time in the 24-hour day.
- ❖ Keep a daily sleep log (see page 165) to monitor your child's progress.

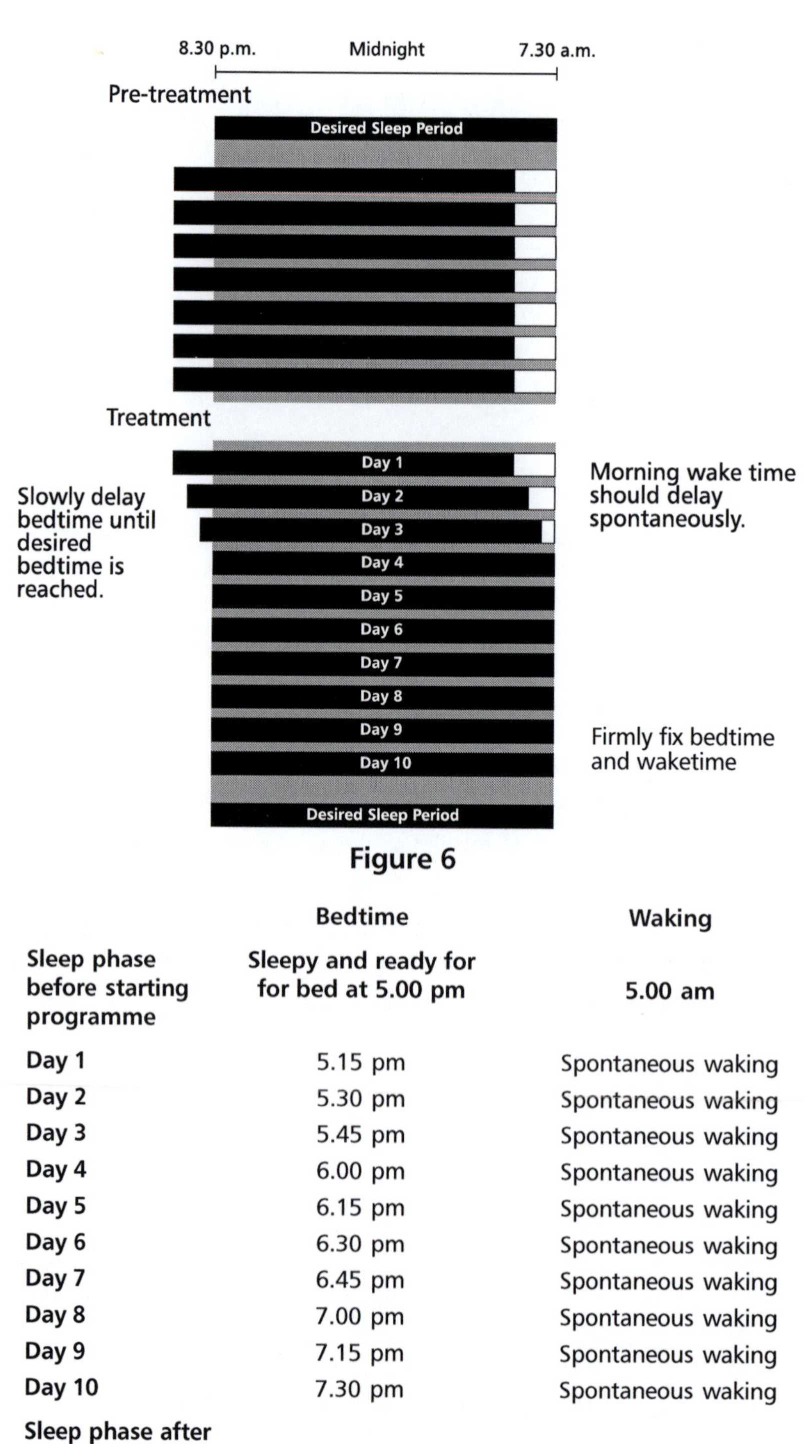

Figure 6

	Bedtime	**Waking**
Sleep phase before starting programme	**Sleepy and ready for for bed at 5.00 pm**	**5.00 am**
Day 1	5.15 pm	Spontaneous waking
Day 2	5.30 pm	Spontaneous waking
Day 3	5.45 pm	Spontaneous waking
Day 4	6.00 pm	Spontaneous waking
Day 5	6.15 pm	Spontaneous waking
Day 6	6.30 pm	Spontaneous waking
Day 7	6.45 pm	Spontaneous waking
Day 8	7.00 pm	Spontaneous waking
Day 9	7.15 pm	Spontaneous waking
Day 10	7.30 pm	Spontaneous waking
Sleep phase after finishing programme	8.30 pm	7.30 am

Figure 7

Insufficient Sleep

Insufficient sleep is a problem that occurs when a young person fails to get enough sleep each night to support normal alert wakefulness during the day. By going to bed regularly too late, the young person is depriving himself of sleep without being aware of it. This results in sleepiness during the day and affects his daytime functioning. Adolescents with daytime sleepiness caused by insufficient sleep usually sleep considerably more at weekends and holidays. If your teenager gets considerably less sleep a night than the chart on page 16 suggests is appropriate, insufficient sleep may be the problem.

What are the symptoms?

- Excessive sleepiness during the day
- Total sleep time is shorter than that expected for the age of the young person
- At weekends or holidays the young person will usually catch up on his sleep by sleeping for longer periods
- Sleep is otherwise normal

Depending upon the extent of sleep loss, other symptoms may develop, including irritability, lack of concentration and attention, reduced motivation, fatigue, restlessness, and loss of appetite.

How common is it?

It is not known how widespread this problem is. Adolescents who are kept up late in the evening or allowed to delay bedtime may develop it. Any factors that lead the young person to delay bedtime and thus reduce total sleep time may be contributary.

When does it start?

This problem mainly occurs in adolescence, when young people choose their own bedtimes.

How long does it last?

If untreated, the problem will continue indefinitely. If sleep loss continues, depression and other psychological difficulties may result.

Is my teenager suffering from insufficient sleep?

Your teenager is probably suffering from insufficient sleep if

- he regularly complains of excessive sleepiness or difficulty going to sleep.

- ❖ his total sleep time is shorter than expected for his age.
- ❖ he sleeps longer at weekends/holidays.
- ❖ the pattern is present for at least three months.
- ❖ if he is allowed to sleep longer for a period of time the problem disappears.
- ❖ there is no underlying medical condition that can account for the symptoms.

Other problems to consider are **poor sleep hygiene**, **limit setting problems**, and **late sleep phase**.

What can I do about it?

You must aim to re-establish an appropriate sleep-wake schedule. Programme 22 gives advice on how to achieve this. It is important to make the young person aware that sleep loss at night severely affects the way he carries out his daytime activities. His daytime routine may need to be modified, allowing more time for homework and shifting relaxation and leisure periods to different times of the day.

Programme 22

Check the chart on page 16 to see how much sleep the young person needs.

- ❖ Decide on an appropriate bedtime and wake time and encourage the young person to keep to them. Check that he does.
- ❖ Keep the bedroom for sleeping in. Discourage activities such as watching television or doing homework in the bedroom.
- ❖ Encourage a winding down period before bedtime, eg playing a tape of relaxing music. The relaxation exercises in Programme 14 may help your teenager to 'wind down' before sleep.
- ❖ Encourage your teenager to maintain the new schedule by praising him the next morning when he has kept to it.

Poor Sleep Hygiene*

Poor sleep hygiene usually occurs in adolescence, when the young person can choose bedtimes for herself. It does not occur in pre-teenage children because at this age parents take the responsibility for the child's bedtime. If you as a parent fail to set firm bedtimes for your child, she may suffer from limit setting problems (see page 119).

It is very easy for a young person to get into poor sleep habits. Researchers have found that some time during the teenage years the circadian rhythm slows down, so that the internal clock is slower than the clock on the wall. The effect of this is that teenagers don't want to go to sleep when the clock says it is bedtime. Their body clocks say that it is much earlier than this. They also have a problem getting up to go to school. When the clock says it's time to get up their body clock still says it's very early in the morning. This pattern continues for several years. This means that it is a constant struggle for young people to keep to the 24 hour schedule that everybody else follows.

What are the symptoms?

- ❖ Difficulty in falling asleep or staying asleep, or excessive sleepiness during the day
- ❖ Daily living activities that are inconsistent with good sleep practices (see below)

Your teenager may fall asleep during the day or sleep excessively several days per week. His bedroom may be chaotic, cluttered, and used for other activities such as doing homework, watching television, etc. Poor sleep hygiene produces daytime symptoms such as irritability and bad temper, reduced attention and concentration, and daytime tiredness.

How common is it?

The prevalence of this problem in unknown, although it is believed to be a fairly common cause of sleep disturbance. Young people who cannot tolerate the daytime consequences of lost sleep will be more susceptible to slip into poor sleep hygiene.

When does it start?

This problem is frequently found in adolescents. Some independence from parents and responsibility for one's own sleep pattern is assumed in the diagnosis, so it is not usually diagnosed in children.

*Inadequate sleep hygiene.

How long does it last?

Poor sleep hygiene may lead to long term sleep problems. For example, if a person gets into the habit of taking naps at different times of the day or drinking too much coffee, eventually these practices will have an impact on sleep.

Does my teenager have poor sleep hygiene?

The teenager may have poor sleep hygiene if

- the complaint is either of sleeplessness or of sleepiness
- she does at least one of the following:
  1. has daytime sleeps at least twice a week
  2. has very variable waking times or bedtimes
  3. has frequent periods (2-3 times a week) of extended time in bed
  4. frequently uses alcohol, cigarettes, or caffeine close to bedtime
  5. exercises too close to bedtime
  6. carries out exciting or emotionally upsetting activities too close to bedtime
  7. uses bedroom for non-related activities (watching TV, eating, studying, etc)
  8. sleeps in an uncomfortable bed
  9. sleeps in a bedroom that is too bright, too stuffy, too cluttered, too hot, too cold, etc
  10. carries out activities requiring a high level of concentration shortly before bedtime (computer games, homework)
  11. spends a lot of time in bed worrying, thinking, or planning
- there is no evidence of illness that accounts for the sleep problem.
- she is not suffering from another sleep problem that produces difficulty in going to sleep, staying asleep, or excessive sleepiness.

Other problems to consider are **environmental sleep disturbance, late sleep phase, irregular sleep-wake pattern**, and **limit setting problems**.

What can I do about it?

If you have a teenager who suffers from poor sleep hygiene, you may have to intervene to encourage her to maintain a more regular schedule. The following programme uses stimulus control and positive reinforcement. Keeping a sleep diary will help you to monitor progress.

Programme 23

You need to help your teenager to regularise her sleep schedule as follows.

1. Regular Sleep Time

Encourage her to establish a regular sleep-wake schedule, especially a regular time of getting up in the morning with no more than plus or minus one hour deviation from day to day including the weekend. The time a person gets up helps to synchronise the circadian rhythm, so it should be early enough for her not to spend a lot of time in bed after waking up. Bedtimes should also be consistent.

2. A Healthy Sleep Environment

If the bedroom is too hot or too cold, sleep will be disturbed. In particular, excessively warm temperatures disrupt sleep. Constant noise can also affect sleep, and it might be necessary to move the young person if her room overlooks a busy road. You should make sure that her room is properly curtained from bright light, and the curtains should be closed. Some young people go to sleep with the radio or television on in their bedroom, and this should be discouraged because the continuous noise during the night will be disruptive. Some find that the radio helps them to relax and fall asleep, and in these cases a clock radio, kept low, which will switch itself off, may be useful.

3. Relaxation Time

It is important to have a wind-down time prior to going to sleep. You should encourage your teenager to change her activities to something relaxing and non-stressful in the half hour or so before bedtime.

4. Stimulus Control

This is an important part of sleep hygiene and consists of removing from the bedroom all stimuli that are not associated with sleep. The bedroom should be used only for sleep. Activities such as eating, drinking, or talking should be done elsewhere because they are associated with arousal and may interfere with going to sleep.

5. Avoid Time in Bed Worrying

Some teenagers spend time before going off to sleep worrying about problems or fretting about not being able to sleep. If the young person finds herself unable to sleep after 30 minutes she should get up and read for a while or listen to soft music from a tape or radio. A warm milky drink sometimes helps. Then when she feels sleepy she should return to bed.

6. Avoid Caffeine

Caffeine (found in both tea and coffee) can profoundly disrupt night-time sleep in some people. If the teenager has poor sleep hygiene she should be careful not to drink either tea or coffee after midday. Alcohol also interferes with sleep patterns.

7. Late Snack

A bedtime snack such as a glass of milk, a biscuit, or a banana may help the teenager to go to sleep. These foods contain tryptophan, which has been found to promote sleep.

8. Regular Exercise

If possible you should encourage the teenager to engage in periods of exercise 20-30 minutes long at least three or four days a week. Experiments have shown that exercise promotes slow wave sleep. However, it should not be carried out within three hours of bedtime.

9. Praise

The importance of rewarding with praise has been discussed on pages 54-55. Reward your teenager with praise every morning when she has tried to bring her schedule under control. After a week of sensible bedtimes you might go on some special outing or give the young person a reward for her efforts.

10. Don't Give Up

If your teenager's schedule has been chronically disrupted it will take time to get it under control. The sleep diary should be filled in every night and you should check it together at the end of each week to see the progress that has been made.

Environmental Sleep Disturbance*

Environmental sleep disturbance is a problem due to a factor in the child's physical environment that keeps her awake or wakes her from sleep. The occurrence of the sleep problem is tied directly to a factor in the environment, such as bright light or noise. When this factor is removed the problem disappears or gradually diminishes.

A variety of factors can cause environmental sleep disturbance. These include excessive heat, cold, noise, light, or movement of a bed partner. Discomfort caused by the use of medical equipment and/or abnormal sleeping patterns associated with a stay in hospital may also result in sleep disturbance, and it is the physical rather than the psychological properties of the environmental factor that cause the problem. The sensitivity of the child to environmental disturbances is a critical factor. Most people are more sensitive to environmental disturbances towards morning, and older people are generally more sensitive than younger ones, although there is considerable variation within age groups.

What are the symptoms?

- Difficulty in falling asleep or staying asleep, or excessive sleepiness during the day
- Other symptoms may include decreased concentration and attention, irritability, and decreased school performance. Physical symptoms such as muscle aches have been reported

How common is it?

This problem is thought to be very common. Living near a busy airport or motorway, or a sleeping environment that is poorly heated or overheated are all predisposing factors.

When does it start?

The problem may occur at any age.

How long does it last?

The problem will continue until the factor causing it is removed.

Does my child have environmental sleep disturbance?

Your child probably has environmental sleep disturbance if

- the sleep problem is associated in time with the occurrence of a set of environmental circumstances that disturb sleep.
- the physical rather than psychological properties of the environmental factors are the main cause of sleeplessness.

*Environmental sleep disorder.

- ❖ removal of the factors results in immediate or gradual return to normal sleep and wakefulness.
- ❖ there is no evidence of illness that could account for the complaint.

Other problems to consider are **poor sleep hygiene, insufficient sleep, irregular sleep-wake pattern**, and **obstructive sleep apnoea.**

What can I do about it?

Follow the advice in Programme 24 on how to improve your child's sleep environment.

Programme 24

Having the right kind of sleep environment can be an important part of sleeping well. A child's bedroom should be made the best it can be in order to make her feel comfortable and relaxed in preparation for sleep. Check the following things in your child's room.

- ❖ Are the sheets fresh and not creased? Are the blankets too light, too heavy, too warm or too cold, too scratchy or too slippery?
- ❖ Do the child's pyjamas/nightgown fit comfortably? Are they suitable for the time of year?
- ❖ Check the child's bed. Is the mattress lumpy? Does it sag in the middle? Is the bed big enough for the child? If these things are a problem, it may be time to buy a new mattress.
- ❖ Are the pillows comfortable?
- ❖ Make sure your child's room is quiet at night. If it is next to a busy main road or other noise, see if your child can change rooms with someone else. Loud noises disturb even good sleepers.
- ❖ Try leaving a window open at night so that the room is well ventilated. However, make sure there is a lock on it so that the child can't get into danger.
- ❖ Your child may be disturbed by too much or too little light. Some children like to sleep in darkness while others are frightened of the dark and want a light. There is no reason why a child should sleep in the dark if she doesn't want to. Try using a low wattage bulb, a dimmer switch, or a night light.
- ❖ Make sure the room is not too hot or too cold. Extremes of temperature disturb sleep.
- ❖ Some children don't sleep well because they feel insecure. It's alright for the child to have the bedroom door open if she is happier with that.

Obstructive Sleep Apnoea

Obstructive sleep apnoea results from breathing problems that occur only during sleep. In children it leads to symptoms of loud snoring during sleep, bed-wetting, restless sleep, morning headaches, and excessive daytime sleepiness. Children with obstructive sleep apnoea often have impaired performance at school and daytime behavioural problems.

What are the symptoms?

- Loud, rasping snoring which occurs every night and can be heard outside the bedroom
- Difficulty breathing during sleep
- Restless sleep
- Repeated episodes of breathing difficulty followed by partial waking with restless movements, briefly improved breathing (with loud snorting or gasping), followed by return to sleep and recurrence of breathing difficulties
- Among children, other symptoms may include bedwetting, daytime sleepiness, irritability, and problems with concentration. Children may have enlarged tonsils or adenoids and be overweight

Children who have this problem display a characteristic pattern consisting of loud snores or brief gasps that alternate with periods of silence lasting 20-30 seconds. The snoring is so loud that it disturbs the sleep of children and parents who are sleeping nearby. The snoring episodes cause partial awakening and disturb the child's sleep patterns. Nightmares and sleep terrors are common. Total sleep time is often long because the child needs to sleep longer to make up for the episodes of apnoea. Children suffer daytime sleepiness because of a lack of continuity of night-time sleep. They may often lapse into short episodes of sleep (microsleeps) during the day which can affect their behaviour and school work. Children who suffer from sleep apnoea often breathe through the mouth and have difficulty swallowing and poor speech articulation.

How common is it?

About 2% of children in the general population are thought to suffer from obstructive sleep apnoea. It is more common in boys and in children who are severely overweight. Children with Down's syndrome, those with neurological problems that lead to upper airway obstruction, and those with enlarged tonsils and adenoids are particularly susceptible.

When does it start?

The average age at diagnosis is 7 years, but the problem probably occurs from infancy.

How long does it last?

This problem will continue until treated.

Does my child have obstructive sleep apnoea?

Your child may have obstructive sleep apnoea if

- he suffers from snuffling, very loud snoring, or choking during sleep.
- he suffers from excessive daytime sleepiness.
- he suffers from one or more of the following: bed-wetting, restless sleep, unusual sleep postures (sleeping on hands and knees, for example), morning headaches, difficulty swallowing, breathing through the mouth, and poor speech articulation.
- Poor school performance and daytime behavioural problems may accompany other symptoms.

What can I do about it?

If you think that your child may suffer from this problem, consult your doctor, who will arrange for tests to be carried out. Some of these can probably be done at home. Research shows that removing the child's tonsils and adenoids relieves symptoms in 70% of children. Children with Down's syndrome may be more difficult to treat because their apnoea sometimes arises from the physical shape of the child's mouth and throat.

Confusional Arousals

Confusional arousals are parasomnias that consist of partial waking from slow wave sleep during the first half of the sleep period. Episodes are sudden and can be quite startling. If you wake your child from slow wave sleep you may trigger an episode if she suffers from this problem. Children may appear awake but do not respond to instructions and resist all attempts to console and reassure them during these episodes. The child may turn over in bed, moan, mutter incomprehensibly, and move about restlessly for a few minutes. She may sit up or look about in a confused manner before returning to sleep. Sometimes the arousal is more violent. The child may begin to crawl around the bed in a confused way. Her eyes will be open but she seems to be unaware of what is going on around her and may fail to recognise you. She may even get up and walk and run about. She may respond to questions with brief answers and allow you to take her back to bed. Young children may well return to sleep without completely waking. Occasionally the partial waking is more violent still. The child may jump out of bed or behave in an agitated, confused, and disorientated manner. She may moan or scream. Usually after a few minutes she will calm down and return to bed. In the morning she will have no memory of the event. During these episodes the child will appear to be both awake and asleep — although her eyes are open and she may speak, she is not able to carry out instructions and she will not recognise you or her surroundings. She is having difficulty making the transition from deep sleep to wakefulness.

What are the symptoms?

- Sudden arousal from sleep
- The child may moan or mumble unintelligibly or thrash about in bed
- The child appears confused and disorientated
- The child appears to be awake but will not respond to the parent
- Attempts to wake the child properly may make symptoms worse

Symptoms usually start before 5 years of age. The child may arouse gradually from slow wave sleep and may moan or mumble incoherently. The symptoms then become more severe. The child may thrash about in bed or fall out of bed. During the episode the child may appear confused, agitated, or aggressive. Attempts to comfort the child only make matters worse. Episodes may last from a few minutes to a few hours and children may not remember the event afterwards.

How common are they?

Confusional arousals occur at some time in almost all children aged under 5 years. They are less common in older children and adolescents, and rare in adults. Anything that causes very deep sleep and difficulty in waking can lead to confusional arousals. Such factors include young age, recovery from sleep deprivation, emotional stress, and medications such as hypnotics, sedatives, tranquillisers, and antihistamines. Confusional arousals are common in children who suffer from sleep terrors and sleepwalking.

When do they start?

The problem usually appears before 5 years of age.

How long do they last?

Confusional arousals usually become less frequent as the child grows older and finally disappear. Until the age of 5 or 6 they are seen as developmental. They are not caused by physical or emotional problems but are reflections of the normal development of the child's sleep stages. If confusional arousals persist into the middle childhood years or even adolescence they may have different causes. Frequent episodes in older children and teenagers are usually due to psychological factors. This does not necessarily mean that your child has serious problems. Some children find it difficult to express their negative emotions during the daytime, and these sometimes come out at night. If the episodes are intense and frequent, however, it may be that your child is under some emotional stress and you should take steps to find out what may be bothering her.

Has my child had a confusional arousal?

Your child may have had a confusional arousal if

- she wakes confused and disoriented.
- confusional episodes can be triggered by waking her.
- she does not appear afraid, and does not sleepwalk.
- the episode is not associated with epilepsy.
- the episode does not fit the description for sleep terrors.

Other problems to consider are sleep terrors and sleepwalking.

What can I do about it?

Although frightening, partial wakings are not usually of significance in children under six years of age. They simply reflect the normal development of your child's sleep stages. Stage IV sleep is very deep in young children and the factors that trigger your child's arousal at the end of the Stage IV sleep cycle are sometimes unable to arouse her fully. She remains half awake and half asleep. Programme 25 offers a set of guidelines on dealing with confusional arousals.

If the wakings persist into the later childhood years or into adolescence they may have different causes and be more significant. Emotional or physical factors are likely to be of importance and it is a good idea to seek help from your doctor. Occasionally partial wakings are confused with nocturnal epilepsy.

SLEEPWALKING (SOMNAMBULISM)

Sleepwalking consists of a complex set of automatic behaviours which result in walking during sleep. It occurs in slow-wave sleep, usually during the first third of the sleep period, within three hours of going to sleep. An episode of sleepwalking usually lasts for less than 15 minutes, and there is rarely more than one per night. The child sits up, gets out of bed, and walks about in a slow, badly coordinated, automatic way. She may engage in more complex activities, such as getting dressed or eating, but these are all done with a lack of awareness. The child may mumble or reply to questions, but the speech is often difficult to understand. If you try to wake a child who is sleepwalking you will find it very difficult — awareness will return only gradually. She may go back to bed and continue to sleep without waking up. Because of the risk of injury, the main goal should be to protect the child from harm. She may walk into dangerous situations, may fall and injure herself, or be injured while trying to 'escape'. Children have been known to walk into the street.

What are the symptoms?

- ❖ Child sits up in bed or walks in sleep, usually during the first third of the sleep period
- ❖ She is difficult to wake during sleepwalking
- ❖ She will not remember sleepwalking when she wakes

Episodes can vary from simple sitting up in bed to walking or running agitatedly round the house. The child may wander about the house, take and eat food, or perform seemingly purposeful tasks. Often the behaviour is bizarre and meaningless. The child may talk but her words will be garbled and incomprehensible. She may appear to be awake but the behaviours she performs are only semi-purposeful. She may be difficult to wake and when awake is frequently confused and will not remember the event.

How common is it?

The incidence of sleepwalking is between 1% and 15% of the general population. The problem is more common in children than in adolescents or adults. A number of factors may trigger these episodes. Stress, anxiety, fever, or sleep deprivation increase the frequency of sleepwalking. Any sleep problem that interferes with slow-wave sleep, such as obstructive sleep apnoea, may lead to episodes of sleepwalking. Having a full bladder also seems to trigger it in young children. Noise has been reported as a triggering factor, as have a number of medications including chloral hydrate. Sleepwalking appears to run in families: if a parent has a history of sleepwalking the chances of a child doing so are six times as great as when neither parent has sleepwalked. Sleepwalking occurs in association with sleep terrors in 10% of cases, and some experts believe them to be variants of the same condition.

When does it start?

Typically sleepwalking begins before the age of 10.

How long does it last?

The problem reaches a peak between 4 and 8 years and usually disappears by the age of 15. Episodes can occur several times a week, or only when triggering factors are present.

Has my child had an episode of sleepwalking?

Your child has probably had a episode of sleepwalking if

❖ walking occurs during sleep.

❖ she is aged is between 4 and 8 years.

❖ she is difficult to arouse during an episode and cannot remember it afterwards.

❖ the sleepwalking is not due to sleep terrors.

Other problems to consider are sleep terrors and confusional arousals. It can be difficult to tell the difference between sleepwalking and problems such as confusional arousals and sleep terrors. Getting out of bed and calm wandering is less common with confusional arousals. Sleep terrors are associated typically with intense panic and fear. The scream that typically starts a sleep terror is not present in sleepwalking.

What can I do about it?

Sleepwalking is a common problem in childhood and need hardly ever be a cause for concern. Programme 25 offers some general advice on how to deal with episodes of sleepwalking. If your child persistently sleepwalks, consult your doctor.

Sleep Terrors

Sleep terrors are quite different from nightmares. The start of a sleep terror is abrupt, shocking, and frightening. The child wakes partially from the deepest part of non-dreaming sleep in the first third of the sleep period, sits upright in bed, and gives a piercing scream. His eyes will be wide open and the pupils dilated, his heart will be beating wildly, and he will appear to be in a state of intense fear. During the episode you will not be able to comfort your child, and any attempts to do so may make things worse. He may get out of bed and run round the room colliding with furniture and walls. He may make unintelligible sounds. If awakened he is confused and disorientated and cannot remember the event. Episodes of sleep terrors usually only last a few minutes and they suddenly subside naturally, with the child swiftly returning to sleep. Next day he will not remember the sleep terror. Sleep terrors should not be confused with nightmares. To distinguish between them, see the table on page 194.

How common are they?

About 3% of children and less than 1% of adults experience sleep terrors. They are more common in boys than in girls and can occur in several members of the same family.

When do they start?

This problem occurs mainly in pre-school children but can occur at any age. In adults it is most common between 20 and 30 years of age. Sleep terrors can be triggered by high fever, sleep deprivation, or certain drugs.

How long do they last?

Sleep terrors are seen mostly in children between the ages of 4 and 12 and usually resolve by adolescence.

Has my child had a sleep terror?

Your child has had a sleep terror if

❖ he experiences a sudden episode of intense terror during a partial arousal from sleep.

❖ the episode occurs during the first third of the sleep period.

❖ he cannot remember the event the next day.

❖ other medical disorders are not the cause of the episode — eg epilepsy.

See the table on page 194 on the differences between sleep terrors and nightmares.

What can I do about it?

Although alarming at the time, sleep terrors need not be a cause for concern. Programme 25 gives general guidelines on dealing with them. Very occasionally sleep terrors are confused with nocturnal epilepsy. If the episodes occur near morning instead of in the first half of the sleep period, if they start with the child waking with the realisation that something is about to happen, or if your child can remember the episode, consult your doctor. If you are worried that your child's sleep terrors are unusually frequent, again, consult your doctor.

Programme 25

Dealing With Confusional Arousals, Sleepwalking and Sleep Terrors

In young children confusional arousals and sleepwalking are probably due to the child's developmental stage and will eventually disappear as he gets older. With older children and teenagers psychological factors are usually important. The child may be under stress and unable to express his emotion during the day, and so at night, when he is 'off guard', his insecurities are expressed in bizarre behaviour. If you have an older child or teenager who is experiencing frequent episodes of thrashing, partial waking, sleepwalking, or sleep terrors, consult your doctor, who may recommend counselling or prescribe medication.

Following these general guidelines may be helpful.

- Make sure your child gets sufficient sleep. Check the amount of sleep required in the chart on page 16. Consider making your child's bedtime a little earlier.
- Make sure your child's sleep and day and night time routines are regular and consistent. Meal times, daytime sleeps, and bedtimes should follow a regular schedule.
- If episodes are frequent and you are concerned about them, or if your child is older than 6 years, consult your doctor.
- Make your child's room and environment as safe as possible to avoid accidental injury. Consider putting a lock high up on doors so that the child cannot get out of the house. Don't leave clutter on the floor or on the stairs. You could try putting a bell on your child's door which will alert you if he leaves the bedroom. For young children you can put a gate on the bedroom door or at the top of the stairs. Don't let the child sleep in the top of a bunk bed.
- If you hear your child, go in and make sure he does not injure himself.
- Let the episode run its course. Keep your distance and don't interfere unless you absolutely have to. Don't shake or try to wake your child. Hold him only if he wants to be held.

Differences Between Sleep Terrors and Nightmares

	NIGHTMARE	SLEEP TERROR
What is it?	A frightening dream that occurs during REM sleep. Full waking follows.	A partial arousal from very deep (Stage IV) sleep.
When does it occur?	In the second half of the sleep period when the child is having the most intense dreams.	In the first third of the sleep period when non-dreaming sleep is deepest.
What is it like?	The child wakes up crying after the nightmare. The child may be anxious and afraid for some minutes.	The child sits up, thrashes, or runs frenziedly about the room with pupils dilated, heart racing, and severe sweating. He may give a piercing scream or cry, talk, or moan. He appears terrified and/or angry. When the child is fully awake the fear and anger vanish.
How does the child respond?	On waking the child will be frightened and/or tearful. He will recognise you and will want to be held, comforted and reassured.	On waking the child will be confused and disoriented. During the episode he will not recognise you or allow you to comfort him. If you try to intervene you may make him more agitated.
How easy is it to return to sleep?	It may take some time to comfort and soothe the child until he is ready to go back to sleep.	Return to sleep is rapid.
Does the child remember the episode in the morning?	The child will remember and describe the dream in the morning (if old enough).	The child will have no memory of the episode.

- Wait until your child seems to be getting calmer and more relaxed and the episode seems to be ending, then help him to lie down and cover him up. Don't try to wake him and ask questions. In the morning, don't make your child feel different by asking questions.
- If your child sleepwalks calmly, talk quietly to him and tell him to go back to bed. He may follow your instructions. If he allows you to touch him without getting upset, lead him quietly back to bed. He may want to go to the bathroom first.
- If your child wakes himself after the episode, don't tease him. Don't mention it in the morning unless he asks. Treat the sleepwalking in a matter of fact way.
- If the sleepwalking is agitated, you will only make things worse if you try to restrain your child. Keep your distance, and only intervene if he is getting into danger. When your child gets calm again, lead him back to bed.
- If your child has had a sleep terror, do not try to wake him. Do not interfere. Stay with him to make sure he does not get into danger. When the screaming subsides, let him return to sleep. Don't question him about the sleep terror in the morning.
- If your child runs about wildly you may have to intervene. Be careful — you may both be injured. Your child may appear angry and aggressive, but remember he is not really awake and is not aware of you. You may make him even more frightened and violent if you are not careful. Talk calmly to your child and stop him getting into dangerous areas of the house. Try not to get hold of him as this can lead to more violent behaviour.
- If there is a possibility of broken windows consider replacing windows with unbreakable glass. Do not have mirrors in the child's room.
- There is a simple and sometimes effective way of dealing with sleep terrors, which is worth trying if your child suffers from them regularly. For a period of days, keep a note of the time your child has a sleep terror. If this happens at a regular time each night, wake the child about 15 minutes before the terror is due, allowing him to go back to sleep after about 5 minutes. If you are not able to tell when an attack is due, but notice your child having the first signs of an attack — increased movement in bed or sweating — you can wake him immediately. After a few nights the sleep terrors will often fade away.
- If your child continues to suffer from frequent sleep terrors consult your doctor. If medication is used it should not be seen as a permanent solution, but mainly as a means of protecting your child from harm.
- If arousals with sleep terrors are frequent, intense, and dangerous, think about having professional counselling, even if your child does not seem to be suffering from emotional stress.

SLEEP STARTS

If you have watched your child fall asleep you may have noticed him give a sudden single brief muscular contraction of the legs. Sometimes children also have contractions of their arms, head, or other postural muscles. They may cry out or mutter. This is called a sleep start. Sleep starts occur during the transition from wakefulness to Stage I sleep. They occur in 66-70% of people and are considered to be benign. They occur with equal frequency in boys and girls and there does not appear to be a family link. Sensory starts, which sometimes accompany sleep starts in older children, include sensory experiences of a dream-like nature and sometimes arouse the child back to wakefulness. They are a part of normal development and do not need treatment.

Sleep Talking

Sleep talking is when the child utters speech or sounds during sleep without being aware of it. An episode usually lasts about 15 to 30 seconds.

Sleep talking in children should be of little concern to parents. This parasomnia is common. Severe outbursts of loud talking in sleep are rare, though they may occasionally disturb parents. Talking to a sleeping child may trigger episodes, though the child will rarely remember the conversation in the morning. Occasionally sleep talking is found in association with sleep terrors, confusional arousals, or sleepwalking.

What are the symptoms?

❖ Talking or making sounds during sleep without being aware of it

How common is it?

Very common in children. Sleep talking that causes major annoyance to others is rare. Sleep talking may be triggered by emotional stress or an illness resulting in a high temperature. Other sleep problems such as sleep terrors, obstructive sleep apnoea, or confusional arousals sometimes trigger episodes. It appears to run in families.

When does it start?

Sleep talking often starts in early childhood.

How long does it last?

Sleep talking may be present for a few days, or last for several months or many years. It is often a normal part of the sleep process.

Has my child had an episode of sleep talking?

Your child has had an episode of sleep talking if

❖ she mumbles or talks during sleep.

❖ she is not aware of talking.

What can I do about it?

Sleep talking is common during childhood and should not overly concern parents. Most children grow out of talking in their sleep as they grow older.

Nightmares and Anxiety Dreams

A nightmare is a frightening dream that wakes the child abruptly from REM sleep, often in the last third of the sleep period. The child will clearly recall the dream and may be very anxious and frightened. The content of the dream usually involves an immediate and believable threat to the child's security, survival, or self-esteem. Talking, screaming, or walking rarely occur during nightmares, and this helps to distinguish nightmares from sleep terrors.

Although they occur during sleep, nightmares are usually caused by or reflect emotional difficulties that have taken place during the day. The anxieties that lead to nightmares are the same as those that produce fears at bedtime and when the child wakes. In young children the concerns are often about separation and loss. Your child may have a nightmare when he first goes to playschool, at a time when you are away from home, or when a new brother or sister arrives. Older children, between 3 and 6, are sometimes concerned about death. They may be afraid that if they go to sleep they will not wake up. This sometimes happens after a death in the family or if a family pet dies. Talking about such losses will help your child to work through them. Nightmares are not common between the ages of seven and eleven, but may arise again in adolescence — a time when new conflicts and anxieties emerge.

What are the symptoms?

- ❖ A long, frightening dream that wakes the child up and leaves him feeling anxious and afraid
- ❖ This usually occurs in the last third of the sleep period
- ❖ The child can remember the dream

How common are they?

Between 10 and 50% of children aged between three and five are estimated to suffer from nightmares often enough to cause their parents concern. Boys and girls are equally affected and nightmares do not seem to run in families. Stress of various kinds, particularly traumatic events, increases their frequency and severity.

When do they start?

Nightmares usually start at 3-6 years but can occur at any age.

How long do they last?

Usually nightmares decrease in frequency as the child gets older. In some children nightmares continue into adolescence and even adulthood.

Has my child had a nightmare?

Your child has had a nightmare if

- he suddenly wakes from sleep with intense fear, anxiety, and a feeling of impending harm.
- he can remember the dream.
- he is fully alert upon awakening, with little confusion or disorientation.
- Return to sleep takes some time and he needs to be reassured.

Nightmares often occur in the longest, most intense REM period during the last third of the sleep period.

Another problem to consider is **sleep terrors**. For the differences between nightmares and sleep terrors see the chart on page 194.

What can I do about it?

Though frightening, nightmares are a normal part of growing up. Programme 26 offers advice on dealing with them.

Programme 26

- If your child wakes you in the night by letting out a terrified scream or comes into your room crying and complaining of frightening dreams, you should give her your attention immediately, regardless of the hour. Nightmares and sleep terrors are dealt with differently, so make sure your child has had a nightmare rather than a sleep terror (see p.194).
- If your child has gone back to sleep when you get to her room, you do not need to wake her. Simply check she is alright and let her continue her normal sleep pattern. If she is asleep but dreaming and is agitated you may be able to comfort her by gently stroking or speaking soothingly to her. Stay until she seems to be peacefully settled again.
- If your child is awake and crying, your main aim should be to offer comfort. Don't allow your child's fear to make you anxious; stay calm yourself and it will be easier to calm your child. Put your arms round your child and talk quietly to her, giving her gentle hugs. It will not hurt to lie down with your child or take her into your bed occasionally. Do not make a habit of this, however, since it can lead to further anxiety and sleep disturbance. You

might distract her by asking if she wants her favourite teddy or a drink of water. Some children like to talk about the dream that scared them, but do not force an unwilling child to tell you the details of a nightmare in the middle of the night.

- ❖ If your child does not want to tell you about the nightmare, don't dismiss it as silly. Acknowledge her fear. Try to explain the concept of a dream as a story that you tell yourself when you are asleep. Children of four or five seem to be able to grasp this idea very well, and you can then encourage your child to 'end' the story on a positive note. You can suggest that the lion was only chasing her because it wanted to make friends, or that the monster took off his terrifying costume and was just her brother underneath. If you do this, be careful not to increase your child's fears and fuel her feelings of insecurity. Don't search the bedroom to prove that the bear has disappeared or look for the monster in all the cupboards.
- ❖ Stay with your child until she is feeling better. If you treat her in a calm and reassuring manner this should not take long since she will be tired and ready to go back to sleep.
- ❖ The following morning you can talk to your child about her fears. You might find out what has been upsetting her and be able to put her mind at rest. Quite often, however, the nightmare is just an isolated event and it will be difficult to work out why it occurred.
- ❖ To help avoid nightmares, don't let your child watch frightening films, TV programmes, or videos — especially just before bedtime. If your child is prone to nightmares, avoid more exciting and frightening bedtime stories and instead read your child's old favourites or play a cassette of songs or music instead. Some children like to have a night light for comfort, or to have their bedroom door left open. Don't take any notice of people who say that your child should be able to go to sleep in the dark. If your child is happier with some light in the room, that's fine.
- ❖ If despite all your efforts to help your child to feel secure she is having frequent and severe nightmares, and particularly if she seems anxious and fearful during the day, you may find that helping your child to relax before bedtime is helpful. The relaxation techniques in Programme 14 may help your child to fall asleep more easily. However, if nightmares still persist it may be necessary to ask your family doctor for advice. It is sometimes helpful for a child to see a psychologist who can work with you to help your child overcome whatever stresses she is experiencing.

Headbanging or Bodyrocking*

Some children rock or roll their bodies in their sleep or bang their heads rhythmically. This problem is known as rhythmic movement disorder. It has several forms. The child may lie prone, repeatedly lifting his head or entire upper body and forcibly banging his head down into the pillow or mattress. He may rock backwards or forwards on hands and knees, banging the front of his head on the bed, headboard or wall, or he may lean back against the wall or headboard, repeatedly banging the back of his head. Sometimes the child rolls his head from side to side. Sometimes headbanging does not occur, but the child rocks his body forwards and backwards. Occasionally rhythmic humming may accompany the movements.

The episodes usually occur as the child falls asleep, during light sleep, or after arousal from sleep, though they sometimes also occur during quiet waking activities, such as listening to music or travelling in a car. Each individual episode usually lasts less than 15 minutes. When the symptoms first begin the movements may not be particularly worrying. They may remain mild and get better naturally, or they may progress to violent activity, shaking the bed, producing loud noises, and waking up other family members. However, though the movements may look violent it is rare for the child to injure himself physically.

What are the symptoms?

- Rhythmic body movements — headbanging, bodyrocking or body rolling — which occur during drowsiness or light sleep

How common is it?

Headbanging occurs in 3-6% of children, bodyrocking in 19-21%, and head rolling in about 6%. It is about four times more common in boys than girls, and the problem sometimes runs in families.

These behaviours often occur in otherwise healthy children. In most children they seem simply to serve the function of soothing or comfort habits like thumb-sucking. It is true that they occur more frequently in children who have sensory impairment, neurological or psychiatric disorders, for example blind children, or those with intellectual impairment or autism, but when headbanging is associated with neurological damage it is almost always clear that the child has an obvious impairment. If your child is developing normally in other ways you have no need to worry if he starts to bang his head or bodyrock.

*Rhythmic movement disorder.

When does it start?

Bodyrocking usually starts at about six months, headbanging at nine months, and head rolling at about ten months.

How long does it last?

This problem commonly occurs in young children and usually gets better in the second or third year of life. Research suggests that some form of rhythmical movement can be observed in two thirds of children by nine months of age. By eighteen months of age this has been reduced to less than 50%, and by four years of age to about 8%. The natural disappearance of symptoms over time as the child gets older lends support to the view held by many sleep specialists that the problem is linked with the child's stage of development. If the symptoms persist into older childhood the problem may be associated with intellectual impairment or autism.

Does my child have problems of headbanging, bodyrocking, or body rolling?

Your child probably has rhythmic movement disorder if

- headbanging, bodyrocking, or body rolling occur during drowsiness or light sleep.
- the symptoms start during the first two years of life.
- there is no evidence of a medical disorder that can account for the symptoms, eg epilepsy.

What can I do about it?

If a baby or toddler starts to headbang or bodyrock there is no need to intervene immediately. Almost certainly the behaviour will disappear quite soon. If, however, the rocking or headbanging is very severe and disrupts the sleep of other family members you may want to try the advice given in Programme 27. Often, however, the headbanging will not disappear completely.

Programme 27

- Do not worry unduly about your child's headbanging or bodyrocking. About 10% of children rock backwards and forwards in bed before falling asleep and about 5% show other rhythmical activities such as headbanging or head rolling, usually at bedtime, after waking at night, or when they wake in the morning. Most of these children are happy and healthy and soon outgrow the behaviours.

- Encourage your child to enjoy plenty of rhythmical activities during the day — using a rocking chair or rocking horse, listening to music, or playing on swings or roundabouts.
- If your child suffers from autism or learning disability and bangs his head vigorously you may want to consider using a helmet or other restraints. Sometimes padding around the bed or cot will reduce the noise and the stimulation your child gets from headbanging. Sometimes placing your child's mattress on the floor will improve matters. We have had some success in reducing headbanging and bodyrocking by replacing the stimulation gained from them with a vibrating toy such as a Vibrotube.* This is placed in the child's bed at night and picking the toy up starts the vibration.
- If your child continues this headbanging or bodyrocking and is not suffering from learning disability you may need to consider whether emotional factors may play a part. Try giving him more attention during the day, while at the same time ignoring his difficult night-time behaviour so you are not providing reinforcement for it. Find some special time for him at bedtime and carry out some pleasant relaxing activities together. You can even try keeping a star chart (see Programme 6) on which you reward quiet nights with a gold star.
- Sometimes headbanging is a way of expressing anxiety. Talk to your child and encourage him to express his worries. Make sure you offer him lots of comfort and reassurance once you know what his anxieties are. If the event that has created the anxiety is very threatening and your child is very upset, you may wish to seek professional counselling.

*These toys can be purchased from Toys for the Handicapped, 76, Barracks Road, Sandy Lane Industrial Estate, Stourport on Severn, Worcestershire, DY13 9QB. Tel: 01299 827820

Sleep Bruxism (Tooth Grinding)

Sleep bruxism is a loud, forceful grinding or rhythmical clenching of the teeth during sleep. It is caused by involuntary contractions of muscles in the jaw. Although the sleeping child will be unaware that it is happening, parents are sometimes disturbed by the noise.

What are the symptoms?

- The child's teeth make a loud grinding noise during the night without the child being aware of it
- Sometimes there is muscle or face pain or headache

Episodes occur in bursts of 5-15 seconds and may be repeated many times during the night. Tooth grinding may cause muscle or face pain or headache. It can produce brief arousals from sleep and may lead to abnormal wear of the teeth.

How common is it?

It is thought that 5-20% of children show the symptoms of tooth grinding, and evidence from dentists shows that it can be identified in 10-20% of the general population. Tooth grinding seems to run in families, and it occurs equally in boys and girls. It seems to be particularly common in children with cerebral palsy or learning disability. It is also more common among children with minor abnormalities of the teeth.

When does it start?

It occurs at all ages but is most common in children.

How long does it last?

Tooth grinding is often associated with stress and anxiety, and lasts as long as the stress lasts. However, it may be chronic without being associated with stress.

What can I do about it?

The most important factor is protection of the teeth. A mouth guard can be worn at night to prevent damage. It will not prevent episodes of tooth grinding, however. If stress or anxiety is a feature, it may be helpful to try to resolve the causes of the stress. Relaxation exercises such as those in Programme 14 may be helpful. There have recently been studies that have used biofeedback to reduce toothgrinding. If you are worried consult your doctor.

Sleep Enuresis (Bedwetting)

Bedwetting is a very common problem that causes a great deal of concern to many parents. It becomes a problem when a child continues to wet at night after most children have become dry. Often parents become angry and frustrated about the bedwetting because they believe that the child is not trying hard enough to be dry. They sometimes punish the child or deny her privileges, hoping to teach her control. When this happens the child soon becomes embarrassed and miserable about her bedwetting but is unable to control it. It often turns bedtime from a relaxed and enjoyable time into a time of stress and anxiety.

The very young child has no bladder control. The child's bladder gradually fills, and when it is sufficiently full it empties spontaneously. By about 16-18 months your child is usually able to tell you that she wants to go to the toilet, though she often does not give you time to respond. By about 18-24 months your child will be able to tell you in time to be taken to the toilet, and by about two-and-a-half years she will be able to go there by herself. When she is about three she may be able to stay dry through the night if she is taken to the toilet in the late evening. By about four-and-a-half years of age about nine out of ten children become dry at night. There is considerable variation in children. If your child has a physical or mental disability, for example, it may take much longer for her to learn to control her bladder. Some very impaired children may never be able to do so. Some children may wet once or twice a week to nightly, and others several times a night.

Bedwetting can occur in any stage of sleep, REM or non-REM. The majority of episodes occur during the first third of the night.

What are the symptoms?

❖ Bedwetting after the age of five (at least one episode per month)

How common is it?

Enuresis occurs in about 30% of four year olds, 10% of six year olds, 5% of ten year olds, and 3% of twelve year olds. One to three per cent of eighteen year olds continue to wet their beds. Bedwetting is more common in children who have been brought up in institutions or have learning disabilities. It is also much more common in boys that in girls and tends to run in families.

When does it start?

Bedwetting should not be a concern until the child reaches five or six years of age. Until that time lack of bladder control is not unusual. Of course, many children are dry at night before then. When bedwetting persists beyond early childhood it often causes embarrassment and inconvenience to both child and parent. The child's activities are sometimes restricted since parents are reluctant to send a child who bedwets to spend the night with friends or go on school trips or camping. The parent finds it a nuisance to have to get up in the night to change the sheets, and often loses patience with the child.

Bedwetting is divided into two conditions: **primary enuresis** is when a child has never achieved bladder control at night, and **secondary enuresis** is when a child who has had 3-6 months of dryness at night begins to wet the bed again. It is important to make this distinction because only primary enuresis is a sleep problem. Secondary enuresis is associated with physical problems (such as urinary infections, sleep apnoea, diabetes or allergies) or with emotional stress (the birth of a new baby, moving house, starting school, and so on). If a physical problem that produces bladder irritability is diagnosed, such as sleep apnoea or an allergy to milk products, treatment often resolves both the sleep problem and the bedwetting.

What are the causes of bedwetting?

There are a number of possible causes of **primary enuresis**, though for a given child it is not possible to say which is most important.

One of the explanations is that bedwetting is the result of having a small bladder. This appears to be supported by the fact that many bedwetters urinate more frequently during the day than other children. However, medical studies have shown that the bladders of children who bedwet are no smaller than those of children who do not. For some reason bedwetters feel the sensation of a full bladder and the need to empty it before the bladder is actually full. Bladder training techniques, one of the ways of dealing with bedwetting, are based on the idea that the bladders of many children who bedwet behave as if they were smaller than they actually are.

A second explanation is concerned with the idea of delayed maturation. This has been suggested as a cause of persistent enuresis. It seems unlikely that children of five or six continue to wet for this reason, however.

A third suggestion is that children wet the bed during dreams. However, laboratory studies have shown that this is not the case. Most bedwetting occurs in the first part of the night during or following an arousal from non-REM sleep. It may be that enuresis is similar to problems of partial waking — in the confusion that follows partial waking from deep sleep, the child urinates without being aware of it. We know that children who have these or other arousals, sleep terrors, or sleepwalking also often wet their beds.

Parents sometimes worry that emotional disturbance may cause the child to bedwet. Although it does sometimes happen that children who have experienced stressful events or had emotional problems start to wet the bed, this usually clears up when the stress stops. Children sometimes have emotional problems as a result of bedwetting because of the embarrassment they feel about the problem.

At the moment the idea that heredity is an important contributing factor in children with enuresis is very popular. It is suspected that a single recessive gene is responsible in children with primary enuresis. This is supported by studies showing that enuresis tends to run in families. There is an incidence of 77% when both parents had this problem as children and 44% when one parent did.

There are a number of possible causes for secondary enuresis. As we have noted, some medical conditions such as diabetes or urinary tract infections can cause bedwetting. Sensitivity to some food has also been suggested, and sometimes night-time wetting decreases when certain foods are eliminated from the child's diet, suggesting that some foods cause bladder irritation.

Does my child have sleep enuresis?

Your child has sleep enuresis if

- she wets the bed during sleep (at least 1 episode per month in children aged 5 or over).

Bedwetting can be associated with medical conditions such as diabetes, urinary tract infection, epilepsy, or emotional stress, or with other sleep problems such as **obstructive sleep apnoea** or **food allergies**.

What can I do about it?

As a general rule you should support and reassure your child, and try to help her not to feel guilty and ashamed. The psychological effect of enuresis can be the most serious complication and can last for many years, far beyond the time when your child wets the bed. If your child is at least five years old and is a persistent bedwetter, there are two programmes you can try to help her achieve bladder control. However, you should check with your doctor first that there is no medical reason for the bedwetting such as a urinary infection or an allergy. Programme 28 uses reward or positive reinforcement and works by praising dry nights and ignoring wet ones. Programme 29 is based on bladder training.

If neither of these programmes works, consult your doctor again. (S)he may be able to offer a 'bell and pad' apparatus to help train your child. This consists of two parts separated by a conductive layer which fits to the bed or is worn inside the pyjamas, connected to an alarm. When the child begins to wet the sheet an electrical connection is made between the two parts and an alarm rings and wakes the child. The apparatus is perfectly safe and works by conditioning. The child learns to associate the feeling of a full bladder with the need to wake. This method should not be used before the age of five or six because it requires your child's full understanding and cooperation. The system should be used every night and you should keep accurate records of the results. You can combine it with a star chart (see Programme 6) on which your child marks her dry nights. The method often takes some months to work. About a quarter of children are dry within 2-6 weeks, 50% by three months, and 90% by six months. Sometimes the child will relapse when you stop using the bell and pad, and you will need to start using it again for a while.

If your child does not respond to behavioural approaches, your doctor may eventually prescribe medication to help control the problem. A drug named Desmopressin has been used successfully to control bedwetting. However, for your child's sake it is best to give the behavioural treatments your best efforts first, since drug treatments sometimes have unpleasant side effects. All medication should be handled very carefully and you should be careful to keep to the prescribed dose.

Programme 28

This first programme is based on reward (positive reinforcement) and can be very effective. You can try this programme with younger children too, but do not use it for a child under three.

- Explain to your child that you want to help him stay dry at night and that you are going to use a star/sticker chart. With your child's help, make a chart from white card, marking on it the days of the week. You will find one to copy on page 129. You will need to buy some packets of circular stickers from a stationer's. On some let your child draw a smiley face and on some a sad face . Each time your child has a dry night, he sticks a smiley face on the chart in the relevant space. If he is not dry in the morning he sticks on a sad face. Encourage your child to do the sticking himself.
- Place the chart in a prominent position where it can be seen easily. This will act as a frequent reminder of the desired behaviour and allow your child to proudly show his progress.
- Always accompany the sticking of a smiley face with praise. Encourage your partner to join in the praise.
- Following nights when your child is wet don't make a fuss, but make sure he puts a sad face on the chart.
- You can add to the reinforcement by giving your child a small toy or reward of his choice for every three smiley faces in a row. When he begins to achieve control of his bladder you can gradually increase the number of smiley faces required to earn a reward.
- Continue the chart until the child has had two months in which he has remained dry (apart from a very occasional accident).

Programme 29

This programme can be carried out on its own or incorporated into a reinforcement programme such as Programme 28. It involves an intensive three week bladder training period before bedtime and three weeks' 'positive practice'. Do not try this programme on children under six years old. Do not force your child to continue with the exercises if she becomes unduly upset while carrying them out.

- Two hours before bedtime, encourage your child to drink some of her favourite drink. The aim is for her to drink about 8oz per hour over the two hour period.
- When your child first reports having to go to the toilet, set a kitchen timer for 5 minutes and ask her to wait until the timer rings.
- As soon as the timer rings, praise your child for her control and allow her to go to the toilet. Encourage her to go on drinking.

- If your child has to go to the toilet before the 5 minutes are up, do not tell her off but encourage her to do better next time. Encourage her to go on drinking.
- After three successive successful trials of 5 minutes, increase the time you ask your child to wait by 5 minutes up to a maximum of 30 minutes. If you find she can easily manage to hold her bladder for 5 minutes you can start the next night on 10 minutes, and so on.
- When it is your child's bedtime, encourage her to go to the toilet before going to bed.
- During the training period, encourage your child to practise starting and stopping the flow of urine while at the toilet at least once a day.
- Continue the increased liquid intake for three weeks.
- At the end of the three weeks, stop giving the increased amount of fluid but continue with the bladder control training every evening, and start a positive practice schedule as follows. When your child says that she wants to go to the toilet, start the bladder control using the timer. She should be able to hold on for about half an hour by now. In the last 5 minutes have your child lie down in her darkened bedroom and pretend to be asleep. She should count to 20 and then get up and go to the bathroom, sit on the lavatory, but not urinate. She should practise this ten times before being allowed to urinate. If she cannot hold on until the tenth practice do not comment. Continue to praise your child for her control when she is successful. Continue the combined bladder control and positive practice for three weeks.

Apnoea of Prematurity and Infancy

Apnoea (periodic breathing) is a breathing problem characterised by three or more respiratory pauses of greater than 3 seconds' duration with less than 20 seconds of normal breathing between pauses. Episodes of periodic breathing can be normal — they can be identified in almost 50% of premature babies — but if they constitute a large proportion of the total sleep time they are considered abnormal. In premature babies, periodic breathing with abnormal apnoeas is called apnoea of prematurity (AOP). Babies who are not premature can have abnormal apnoea too. Apnoea of infancy (AOI) is present when breathing ceases for 20 seconds or longer or when breathing cessation is less than 20 seconds but is accompanied by rapid heartbeat, abrupt marked pallor, or 'blue' appearance. If your baby suffers from apnoea of prematurity or infancy it will almost certainly have been diagnosed at birth and the hospital doctor will have given you advice on how to deal with it. If you are present when your baby suffers a significant episode of apnoea, seems to stop breathing or goes blue, this is a medical emergency. Doctors call it an apparently life threatening event (ALTE). You will need to call an ambulance straight away and perhaps use resuscitation techniques which will have been taught to you by your doctor or health visitor.

What are the symptoms?

- Repeated episodes where breathing stops for more than 20 seconds during sleep
- During episodes the baby suffers marked pallor or goes 'blue'
- The baby may become 'floppy'
- Episodes are often accompanied by rapid heartbeat

How common is it?

Estimates of apnoea of prematurity before 31 weeks' gestation are between 50 and 80%. After 31 weeks, apnoea is reported in 12-15% of infants.

When does it start?

Apnoea of prematurity begins after the first one or two days of life. Apnoea of infancy usually starts between 4 to 8 weeks of age.

How long does it last?

Apnoea of prematurity disappears by 36 weeks postconceptional age in most cases, but periodic breathing may persist for up to three months.

What can I do about it?

If your baby suffers from apnoea of prematurity or infancy this will usually have been diagnosed at birth. The hospital paediatrician will have given you advice about it, and you may have been provided with a monitor to alert you if your child stops breathing. Monitors ring an alarm and flash a light when breathing movements stop for longer than 20 seconds. There are three types. One is a sensor pad attached to the baby's stomach, one is a pressure pad or mattress on which the baby lies, and one consists of electrodes which are attached with tape to the baby's chest. Monitors are often provided if the baby has has an ALTE or the parents have already suffered a cot death. While they provide some comfort from anxiety they do have disadvantages. They are prone to false alarms and some parents become dependent upon them and find it difficult to stop using them. So far there is no direct evidence that monitors reduce cot death.

Eventually most babies outgrow the condition. If you think your baby may have this condition and it has not been diagnosed, consult your doctor without delay. Remember, this is a very rare problem of prematurity and very early infancy.

Colic

Colic is not in itself a sleep problem. It affects otherwise healthy babies in the first few months of life. The child has rhythmical attacks of piercing screaming which usually occur in the evening or late afternoon. She will draw up her legs as if in pain and will often continue to cry for several hours. Colicky babies are very difficult to comfort. You may walk about with them or rock them, but often nothing seems to help. Sometimes passing wind or having a bowel movement seems to relieve the pain. If the colic is severe, your doctor may prescribe medication to help relax your child's bowels and ease the discomfort.

Some doctors do not believe in colic; they point out that all babies draw their legs up when they cry and are bound to pass wind. When the child cries loudly she swallows air, which causes pain and discomfort. Thus the wind and pain are caused by, not causes of, the screaming. Other doctors are firm believers in colic. They believe that the condition is a genuine one caused by gas blocked in loops in the bowel.

What are the symptoms?

- ❖ Violent rhythmical screaming attacks which start during the third or fourth week of life and end by four months of age
- ❖ Attacks generally start between 5 and 8pm and end by about midnight
- ❖ During the attack the child does not respond to comfort from her parents
- ❖ Physical movements occur during the attack. The body stiffens, the fists are tightly clenched, the legs are drawn up, and the child writhes and twists. The baby looks as if she is in severe pain
- ❖ Daytime sleep is irregular and brief

How common is it?

About one in five babies has been found to suffer from colic in the early months.

When does it start?

Symptoms usually begin in the third or fourth week of life.

How long does it last?

Colic usually gets better by three to four months.

Does my child have colic?

Other problems to consider are **limit setting problems, incorrect sleep associations, irregular sleep-wake patterns,** and **food allergies**.

What can I do about it?

Intolerance to cow's milk has been suggested as a cause. The evidence is not conclusive, but if colic persists in your baby you may like to try excluding cow's milk either from her diet if she is bottle fed or from your own diet if she is breast fed. If the colic is severe, your doctor may prescribe medication to help relax your child's bowels and ease the discomfort.

Sometimes a colicky baby is one who is overly sensitive to events going on around her. This may lead to a build-up of tension during the day. Some doctors believe that the child needs an opportunity to discharge the tension by crying. If your baby seems to have colic and cannot be comforted and you have tried eliminating cow's milk from her diet, you may try allowing her to cry for 15-20 minutes in her cot. If after this time she is still unsettled, comfort her gently and quietly. Avoid rocking and bouncing her around, or other vigorous handling — just hold her gently. If this does not work, allow her to cry for another 15-30 minutes. Then try comforting her again. You will probably find that the crying episodes will decrease within a few days.

Colicky infants often go on to develop true sleep problems. These problems appear to be the same as the ones they had up to four months of age, but they are not. The habits that the child forms when she has colic often persist after the colic itself has disappeared. You may have given a great deal of attention to your child while she had colic. You may have rocked her, cuddled her, and walked her up and down to try to comfort her and help her to fall asleep. The child easily comes to expect to be held, rocked, or cuddled until she falls asleep. If this happens you will have to help your child to learn new associations for falling asleep. Programmes 7-10 will help you to do this.

How do you decide when the colic has gone? One study found that 54% of babies had stopped having attacks by two months, 85% by three months, and 100% by four months. You can take this as a guide. Remember that colic also occurs during the day, not just at the child's bedtime. A colicky baby seems to be in real pain. So if your child cries mainly when you put her to bed, if she does not seem to be in real pain, and if she stops when you pick her up, then the colic has probably disappeared. She still enjoys the attention she has been getting and will make a fuss unless you take steps to correct her sleep associations.

Two Other Common Problems That Cause Sleep Disturbance

Teething

Parents often believe that teething pains are the cause of a child's night waking. While it is true that teething pains can affect the child's sleep and cause her to sleep poorly for several nights, teething does not cause sleep problems that go on for many weeks as some parents might think. Sometimes teething may have been the original cause of a child's getting into bad sleep habits, but the attention that the child gets from her parents at night encourages the problem to continue. Waking up has become a habit. When this happens you may need to encourage your child to settle to sleep quietly by carrying out a sleep programme. Try Programmes 7-10.

Middle Ear Infection

Acute middle ear infection is one of the most common childhood illnesses and does not often go unrecognised. The cause of the child's sleep complaint is clear. By contrast, chronic middle ear infection is sometimes present despite the child having few symptoms except the disruption of sleep.

Children with acute middle ear infection suffer from pain, fever, changes in appetite, and vomiting. The child wakes frequently at night, often for a long time, and is consequently sleepy in the daytime. If you think your child may be suffering from this condition, you should consult your doctor immediately so that (s)he can prescribe antibiotics.

Chronic middle ear infection is often associated with few symptoms. The child's hearing may be decreased, but not noticeably so. Despite this the child's sleep may be significantly disrupted and it is always wise to consult your doctor if a child who has been sleeping well suddenly begins to suffer night wakings. It is very easy for parents of children who have had acute or chronic middle ear infection to forget the basics of sleep hygiene, which we talked about on page 26. While their child is being treated for an ear infection parents should be careful to keep to regular bedtimes and morning waking times. It is easy for sleep disruptions originally caused by ear infections to become habitual.

INDEX

A

ABC analysis 50, 53, 57, 60
ABC chart 51, 57-59, 68, 81
Adjustment sleep disorder
    (see Difficulty adjusting to stress)
Advanced sleep phase syndrome
    (see Early sleep phase)
Allergies 14, 18, 35-37, 160, 161, 206, 207, 213
    (see Food allergies)
Antecedents of behaviour 57, 61
Antibiotics 36, 37, 215
Anxieties or night-time fears 140
Apnoea 90, 185, 186, 200, 208-210, 214, 215
    (see Obstructive sleep apnoea)
Apnoea of prematurity and infancy 211

B

Bedtime behaviour 61, 65, 69, 73-77
Bedtime routines 25, 29
Bedwetting 11, 24, 39, 185, 205-208
    (see Sleep enuresis)
Bodyrocking 90, 99, 103, 111, 201-203
Brain damage 37, 38
    (see Neurological problems)

C

Chronic illness 13, 18, 35, 162
Circadian rhythms 33, 162
Colic 35, 83, 86, 160, 161, 213, 214
Confusional arousals 39, 187-189, 191, 193, 197
Controlled crying technique 72
Cot death 117, 212
Cow's milk allergy 5, 160

D

Delayed sleep phase syndrome
    (see Late sleep phase)
Depression 13, 34, 119, 177
Development of sleep stages 22
Diabetes 206, 207
differences between sleep terrors and nightmares
    94, 95, 100, 102, 103, 109-112, 199
Differences Between Sleep Terrors and Nightmares
    194
Difficulty adjusting to stress 34, 91, 96, 109, 132,
    149, 150
Dreaming 192, 200 *(see REM sleep)*

E

Ear infections 131, 215
Early sleep phase 33, 43, 88, 94, 96, 101, 163,
    174
Environmentalsleep disorder
    (see Environmental sleep disturbance)
Environmental sleep disturbance 97, 106, 108,
    180, 183
Epilepsy 14, 36, 37, 189, 192, 193, 202, 207
Extinction 55, 56, 60, 61, 64, 67-71, 73

F

Fears *(see Anxieties or night-time fears)*
Feeding *(see Night-time feeding problems)*
Food allergies 35, 160, 161, 207, 213
Food allergy insomnia *(see Food allergies)*

G

Gradual programme of change
    (see Graduated extinction)
Graduated extinction 61, 67, 71-73

H

Headbanging or Bodyrocking 201
How Common Are Sleep Problems 12
Hyperactivity 35, 36

I

Incorrect sleep associations 31, 46, 83, 86, 91, 93,
    109, 120, 122, 130, 132, 135, 150, 156, 213
Insufficient sleep 33, 43, 89, 98, 105, 107, 108,
    119, 132, 175, 177, 184
Irregular sleep-wake pattern 33, 44, 83, 87-89, 92,
    94, 96, 97, 101, 105, 106, 109, 120, 132,
    162, 163, 168, 180, 184, 213

L

Late sleep phase 33, 43, 84, 89, 92, 97, 101, 105,
    107, 109, 120, 132, 163, 166-168, 171, 173,
    178, 180
Learning disability 38, 203, 204
Limit setting problems 91-93, 119-121, 132, 150,
    156, 163, 168, 175, 178-180, 213
Limit setting sleep disorder
    (see Limit setting problems)

M

Mattresses 117, 118
Medical conditions 25, 35, 83, 85, 89, 91, 93, 97,
    107, 108, 132, 163, 178, 207
Medication 83, 86, 97, 107, 108, 116, 191, 193,
    195, 208, 213, 214
Mental handicap/disability *(see Learning disability)*
Middle ear infection 35, 215

N

Naps 23, 26, 44, 46, 83, 87-89, 92, 94, 96, 97,
    101, 105, 106, 109, 169, 180
Negative reinforcement 55
Neurological problems 37, 89, 97, 107, 108, 162,
    167, 185
Night terrors *(see Sleep terrors)*
Night-time behaviour 14, 46, 50, 51, 54, 57-61,
    67, 73, 115, 128, 203
Night-time fears 34, 91, 94, 120, 140-142, 144,
    150
Night-time feeding problems 87, 155, 156, 158,
    159
Nightmares and Anxiety Dreams 198
Nocturnal eating/drinking syndrome
    (see Night-time feeding problems)
Non-REM sleep 21-24, 207

O

Obstructive sleep apnoea 35, 36, 43, 95, 97, 99, 104, 106, 112, 184-186, 191, 197, 207

P

Parasomnias 36, 38, 39, 43, 187, 197
Parental Expectations 32, 39
physical or mental handicap/disability *(see Learning disability)*
Poor sleep hygiene 105-108, 119, 168, 178-180, 182, 184
Positive reinforcement 53, 54, 61, 64, 66, 68, 69, 71, 73, 75, 107, 108, 121, 123, 126, 128, 132, 133, 137, 142, 143, 164, 180, 208, 209
Problem behaviour 50, 51, 53, 69, 70
Providing the conditions that encourage sleep 61, 65, 73
Punishment 55-57, 60, 74, 75, 119, 141

R

Relaxation techniques 142, 152, 200
REM sleep 22,-24, 39, 198
Rewards 56, 61-64, 68, 74, 76, 122, 123, 125, 128, 136, 152
  rules for rewards 122, 134
Rhythmic movement disorder *(see Headbanging or bodyrocking)*

S

Setting limits for bedtime behaviour 28
Settling problems 12, 13, 25, 28, 34, 42, 45, 93, 109, 127, 166
Sleep apnoea *(see Obstructive sleep apnoea)*
Sleep associations 31-33, 38, 42, 43, 46, 121, 124, 130-132, 135, 151, 157, 214
Sleep bruxism 39, 99, 103, 112, 204
Sleep cycles 121, 122
Sleep cycles in children 23
Sleep deprivation 188, 190, 192
Sleep diary 7, 32, 34, 37, 51, 125, 136, 144, 152, 162, 168, 175, 180, 182
Sleep enuresis 39, 95, 103, 205, 207
Sleep history 41-46
Sleep hygiene 26, 35-37, 85, 89, 97, 179, 181, 215
Sleep latency 41
Sleep log 163, 164, 169, 171, 175
Sleep needs 16
Sleep onset association disorder *(see Incorrect sleep associations)*
Sleep patterns 13, 14, 18, 21, 22, 30, 32, 35, 37, 38, 49, 105, 106, 108, 109, 115, 116, 121-123, 126, 134, 138, 139, 161, 164, 169, 182, 185
Sleep patterns in babies 22
Sleep problems 11-14, 17, 18, 21, 25, 33-41, 49, 65, 68, 71, 81, 120, 142, 160, 180, 197, 207, 214, 215
Sleep rhythms 33, 37
sleep stages 23, 188, 189
Sleep starts 38, 196
Sleep talking 38, 43, 99, 103, 111, 197
Sleep terrors 11, 24, 36, 38, 39, 43, 141, 185, 188, 191-193, 195, 197-199, 207
Sleeping in parents bed 27
Sleepwalking 22, 24, 36, 38, 39, 99, 102, 111, 188, 190, 191, 193, 195, 197, 207
slow wave sleep 182, 187
snoring 35, 185, 186
Stage I sleep 21, 196
Stage II sleep 21
Stage III sleep 22, 39
Stage IV sleep 22, 36, 189
Stress *(see Difficulty adjusting to stress)*

T

Target behaviour 50, 51
Teething 11, 35, 116, 215
Tooth grinding (see Sleep bruxism)
Toys for the handicapped 63, 203

W

Waking problems 11-13, 24, 31, 34, 36, 38, 72, 76, 130, 135, 140, 141
What are sleep problems 11
Why sleep problems arise 25